PENGUIN BOOKS
YARAANA

Born in 1947 to a Zoroastrian business-family in Bombay, India, Hoshang Merchant graduated second in his BA Class (1968) with a major in English and a minor in the culture of India. From his mother's family he descends from a line of preachers and teachers. He holds a Master's from Occidental College, Los Angeles. At Purdue University he specialized in the Renaissance and Modernism. Anais Nin and he corresponded for four years. His book on Nin, *In-discretions*, earned him a Ph.D from Purdue in 1981 and is published by Writers Workshop which has also published eight books of his poetry since 1989. He helped establish the Gay Liberation at Purdue. Since leaving Purdue in 1975, Merchant has attended the Provincetown Fine Arts Work Centre, Massachusetts and lived and taught in Heidelberg, Iran and Jerusalem where he was exposed to various radical student movements of the Left. He has studied Buddhism at the Tibetan Library at Dharamsala, north India, as well as Islam in Iran and Palestine. Rupa and Co. published his book of poems *Flower to Flame* in 1992 in the New Poetry in India series. Currently he teaches Poetry and Surrealism at Hyderabad University and is unmarried by choice.

Yaraana

Gay Writing from India

Edited by Hoshang Merchant

PENGUIN BOOKS

Penguin Books India (P) Ltd., 11 Community Centre, Panchsheel Park,
New Delhi 110 017, India
Penguin Books Ltd., 80 Strand, London WC2R 0RL, UK
Penguin Putnam Inc., 375 Hudson Street, New York, NY 10014, USA
Penguin Books Australia Ltd., 250 Camberwell Road, Camberwell,
Victoria 3124, Australia
Penguin Books Canada Ltd., 10 Alcorn Avenue, Suite 300, Toronto,
Ontario, M4V 3B2, Canada
Penguin Books (NZ) Ltd., Cnr Rosedale and Airborne Roads, Albany,
Auckland, New Zealand

First published by Penguin Books India 1999

Typeset in *Palatino* by Digital Technologies and Printing Solutions, New Delhi
Printed at Chaman Offset Printers, New Delhi

Page 212 is an extension of the copyright page.

To my lovers
past present and future.

To the past ones for our ignorance
to the present ones for our struggle
to the future ones in the hope
that a new Indian male will birth

If you should come in dreams to free me of dreams
Or, give me heart-fire to dream my dreams

You kill me with your tears of longing
Someone give your hard-heartedness some watery dreams

You finished me off with your slightly parted lips
If not with a kiss at least reply in words to my dreams

Give us wine if hatred be yours
If not the cup give us the wine of dreams

Asad! His limbs swelled with pride
When he said 'Press my limbs'

—Ghalib
translated by Hoshang Merchant

Contents

Acknowledgements   x

Introduction   xi

Public Meeting and Parting as Private Acts   1
  Firaq Gorakhpuri

The Contract of Silence   2
  Ashok Row Kavi

Shivraj   26
  Kamleshwar

Pages from a Diary   34
  Bhupen Khakhar

O Pomponia Mine!   37
  Sultan Padamsee

Epithalamium   39
  Sultan Padamsee

And So to Bed   44
  Sultan Padamsee

The Jungle   46
  Madhav G. Gawankar

The Slaves   49
  Hoshang Merchant

Poems from a Vacation   55
  S. Anand

Night Queen   57
  Mahesh Dattani

Gandu Bagicha   72
   Namdeo Dhasal
Moonlight Tandoori   76
   R. Raj Rao
A Mermaid Called Aida   87
   A Review
from Waiting for Winter   90
   Belinder Dhanoa
Underground   97
   R. Raj Rao
Opinions   99
   R. Raj Rao
Bomgay   100
   R. Raj Rao
Beta   101
   Rakesh Ratti
Sunshine Trilogy   102
   Owais Khan
from Trying to Grow   106
   Firdaus Kanga
from The Golden Gate   115
   Vikram Seth
Six Inches   131
   R. Raj Rao
Karate   145
   Adil Jussawalla
The Raising of Lazarus   147
   Adil Jussawalla
Song of a Hired Man   148
   Adil Jussawalla
'Never Take Candy from a Stranger!'   152
   Gyansingh Shatir
from Sheltered Flame   158
   Iqbal Mateen
from Yayati   161
   Vishnu Khandekar

Desire Brings Sorrow   163
    Dinyar Godrej
Under Water   164
    Dinyar Godrej
On the Road to Jata Shankar   168
    Dinyar Godrej
Apparently   170
    Dinyar Godrej
※ Rite of Passage   171
    Manoj Nair
※ The Sweetest of All   180
    Frank Krishner ⟵ Indian?
Knowing Your Place   189
    Ian Iqbal Rashid
※ Autobiography   192
    Hoshang Merchant

Afterword   204
Biographical Notes   207

Acknowledgements

My gratitude to the following:
Firstly to V.K. Karthika, a former student of mine and associate editor at Penguin India for dreaming up this book and thinking of me ten years since I taught her as an editor for India's first gay anthology.

To S. Viswanathan for his support.

To Mughni Tabassum for help with Urdu poetry.

To Aloka Parasher Sen for advice on Ancient India.

To K. Narayana Chandran for much advice and encouragement.

To Padmakar Dadegaonkar for help with the Marathi novel.

To Mamta Sagar for help with the Kannada section.

To my student-friend N. Vardarajan, MA (Philosophy) for trekking to the library for me for months.

To Rajendra Gowd for typing this manuscript.

To A. Giridhar Rao for all his help.

Lastly yet most importantly to Jameela Nishat who took an active interest at every stage of the book's progress to completion and for a decade of unstinting friendship and support.

Introduction

My interest in India's homosexual literary history is more than personal. It is also more than sociological and more then mere academic interest in a queer aspect of culture studies.

There is no such beast in zoology as a 'homosexual'. It is an invention of late nineteenth century European science, half Greek (Grk. 'homo' = 'same') and half Latin ('sexual' being Latin in root). It denotes not a person but a category that several sensitive persons, obliging science, have tried to fit themselves into. NRI gays in *Trikone* (San Jose, California) have concocted a terminology for Gays: 'Samlingan' for the sexuality, 'samlingia' for 'homosexual', i.e., a literal translation of Western terms. Such a term does not exist in India where the practice is not codified, only quietly condoned and above all, not talked about. As Foucault reminds us in *History of Sexuality*, sex is not modern, talking about it is.

I use the term 'homosexual' as a descriptive term, descriptive of a sexual practice and of its concomitant world view (because you are what you do or don't do in bed) much as I use the words 'lesbian' or 'prostitute' as descriptive nouns rather than as words of opprobrium. I must admit I have trouble with the word 'gay'. 'Show me a happy homosexual and I'll show you a gay corpse', was a self-hating taunt in the sixties' homosexual Broadway play *Boys in the Band*. I have known reasonably happy homosexuals though I do not consider myself one. I have also known other unhappy homosexuals just as I have known terribly unhappy heterosexuals. So, the term 'gay' is nonsensical. I resent gay as a category as it is a political one. Octavio Paz says gay liberation and women's liberation are political movements and have nothing to do with human liberation (which is the precinct of art). I fully agree with Paz.

Every culture looks at this group in its own way. Islam's strict strictures on any sex outside heterosexual polygamous marriage and strict social segregation of the sexes has spawned both homophobic guilt plus a vast literature of homosexuality.

> My youth goes like this
> Time just goes like this
> Green green glass bangles
> beside my bed
> My blouse is on fire
> My youth just goes like this
> Who is to tell him, that Aulia Nizammuddin
> You try now, I've been trying all the time
> Time just goes like this
> My youth goes like this.

'Bandhish' by Amir Khusro (1253-1325)

India's Hindu culture which is a shame culture rather than a guilt culture, treats homosexual practice with secrecy but not with malice. Many educated Indians confuse 'homosexual' with 'eunuch'. They think homosexuals lack sexual organs or cannot sustain erections. Many passive homosexuals even today are forced to live with eunuchs if not become eunuchs through castration. I have known educated passive gay men from elite families who think it a shame to ask for any penile gratification from their macho partners. You can call it a state of voluntary mental self-castration. The passive homosexual, however, is possessed by the mother-image. They have learnt their mothers' childhood injunctions against having sex with women. Mother, however, forgot to say, 'Do not have sex with men either.' And the gay son found a way out of his woman-conundrum. This prohibition/obedience syndrome breeds an ambivalent attitude in the young boy towards mother in particular and to women in general. Either you worship the Madonna or the Mother Goddess as in Latin (or Hindu) cultures or you denigrate women as in the Anglo-Saxon (or Muslim) cultures. These opposing tendencies are marked in the homosexual sub-culture. Either gay men love older women (Liz Taylor/Rekha) or impossibly unavailable women (Madhuri Dixit/Marilyn Monroe) or women martyred like themselves, their mothers, or Meena Kumari, or again, Monroe. It is not an accident that most of these icons have gay image-makers. They are literally an invention of the gay man, viz., the dress-designer, hair stylist, choreographer or the make-up man. In that sense Hollywood culture is a creation of the gay male. Gay men have created impossibly alluring women who may never be seduced like one's own mother. They have fed the fantasies of the general populace for generations. Pop culture is a creation largely of homosexuals.

New York University's Performance Theory department is largely run by gays. In essence performance theory states that sexuality, or one's sexual persona, the way one comes onto society or projects one's sexuality socially is only a performance. Gay sex, all sex roles, all genders are a performance. Bachchan's macho man is a performance. Meena Kumari's suffering woman is a performance. All women suffering like Meena, our mothers included, with all due respect to them, are performing. Gender is socially constructed.

In India, the MTV culture has done the country's homoerotic culture a disservice. It has projected plastic women like Sophiya Haq and Alisha Chinai onto the adolescent male imagination, depriving them of the solaces of yaraana. Secondly, it has projected the West's gay sub-culture in its worst light by highlighting its lunatic fringe as if it were the mainstream. Your baker, butcher, banker, bus conductor, neighbour or brother could all be very ordinary and also very gay. It has also caused a backlash. While encouraging homosexuals to come out of the closet and increasing tolerance and acceptance it has also caused an increase in the display of physical or verbal abuse against homosexuals and put closet homosexuals on the defensive. It has also put many young men out of the gay circuit, forcing them prematurely into the arms of women.

Another heart-wrenching aspect of homosexual liberation in India is the distance and sometimes outright hostility between gays and women. Gays and women are fighting the same oppressor, the macho male. Ideally I should be joining hands with the prostitute my bisexual lover frequents in teaching him a lesson or two in liberation but instead I beat her out of my house because I see her as a competitor. Old habits die hard. My woman colleague fighting for her rights instead of respecting me for identifying with women even to the extent of referring to myself in Hindi in the feminine gender mocks me because she herself identifies with the male establishment which patronizes her. That is where the power lies. But power is never given away, it has to be snatched.

In a superficially politicized world a gay faces poignant choices. James Baldwin had to choose between his Black community and his White lovers. (He played out the sado-masochistic White Master/Black Slave saga over and over in his lovemaking and his stories.) The blacks rejected him as did the white liberal establishment for his psychological inability to make love to a black man. In our context today, a Selvadurai has to choose between his Sri Lankan citizenship and a Tamil lover in an island-nation torn by ethnic strife. This makes for good literature even if it's a bad life.

I would here like to include two local news stories that appeared in the press recently. A forty-nine-year-old teacher, a Christian, bashed in the head of his eleven-year-old Muslim boy-student for refusing his homosexual advances. The teacher was given a mere one-year jail sentence. In another incident, a fourteen-year-old castrated an eleven-year-old boy for refusing to satisfy his urges. The eleven-year-old's organ was reattached by microsurgery involving forty stitches. Would not education of both the offender and the victim solve the problem of gay rape? Is gay rape any different from a woman being raped? Why do those who protest rape never talk of gay rape? Why this conspiracy of silence? The passive gay is subjected to the same humiliation while walking down a street as a woman is in India. In the land of political correctness they snigger behind my back these days. What's the difference?

The difference is that a passive homosexual is nominally a man while a woman is a woman, man's other. The passive homosexual, discarding male heterosexuality and lacking any other discourse, becomes a woman, caricatures a woman. He is caught in a binary bind: you can either be master or slave, no third thing which is a free agent, the creation of which is any liberation movement's goal.

This hatred of the homosexual, I think, goes back to the Judaic, Zoroastrian, Christian, Islamic injunctions against oral or anal sex as being 'unproductive', 'sterile'. The fertility/sterility duality is economic in origin. It has something to do with production—production of babies who become men who produce more babies for whom more baby-food and baby-shoes have to be produced. In times of scarcity these same babies termed 'men' at sixteen will march to war and become cannon-fodder. The homosexual refuses to be a part of this brutality. His sex-play is not for creation but mere recreation. He has, therefore, to be crushed.

Marriage, then, at least for the homosexual, is passé. Love in a dark world is not. Homosexuality as it is known in the West does not exist in India. Most men are bisexuals. Or, to put it another way, most homosexuals get married due to societal pressures. Some commit suicide. Most adjust to a double life, so do their wives. One would imagine in such cases the husband continues his pre-marital sex habits and a divorce does not ensue. There is no greater misery in such marriages than in most Indian marriages which are arranged. Yet, youthful friendships up to but not including homosexuality are common for India's men. They call it yaraana or dosti. It is a *blutbruderschaft,* a blood brotherhood, a bond between males of equal stature and social standing usually.

The heterosexuals have learnt 'living-in' and the 'sex-club' culture from the homosexuals. Homosexuals have learnt about love from heterosexual literature at school, for love is a literary genre. Now we are producing our own homosexual literature. Worse, like Pater and Housman and Arnold, we have contributed to mainstream high culture while masquerading under straight poses. The problem with India's gay literary elite is that most of them (here I'm talking of Indian writers in English) are still in the closet. Some do not wish to be identified as gay in a gay anthology as it would limit the literary scope of their work. Fair enough. But fear of a witch-hunt is the main cause. Certain authors, Anais Nin for instance, are heroes because they stand up and speak about their condition and about how they overcame it through art (not politics, but art) thereby inspiring others like myself in a similar condition to try to transcend our destinies. Because anatomy is no longer destiny, as Genet would have us believe. That does not mean the gay writer does not write his struggle or is not seen publicly struggling. My detractors tell me, 'You are a textbook case of why a young man would choose not to become homosexual.' In reality no one can be induced to 'become' homosexual. 'I had no more choice in my sexuality than a Negro does in choosing his skin colour,' Genet wrote. This bespeaks a humility before the mystery of our sexualities that all our knowledge has still not solved. And, there is no remedy for a closed heart.

The new gay academic mafia, like the feminist or communist academic mafias, tends to fit all literature into a form of their own special pleading. Yes, Virginia, there is a Santa Claus and there is a literature above one's own special pleading, the sonnets of Shakespeare, for example, being products of genius rather than homosexual mania.

Lest I be accused of intellectual bad faith I have to add that intellectual freedom is finally inseparable from political freedom, and what Pier Paolo Pasolini's communist gay poetry could not achieve for the Firulian peasant was achieved by the bourgeoisification of the peasant under Italy's post-War free market.

In this book I try to avoid the old categories and of course will commit the sin of inventing newer and I hope, broader and less offensive categories of the literature of male bonding, as found in India.

The oriental male like the oriental gods is polymorphous perverse. Sexuality in the East has always been a continuum rather than a category. There are a variety of gods in the non-Islamic East and it is nothing but arrogance in this world to say there is only one god or to say there is only one sexual play.

I, a male homosexual Parsi by religion, Christian by education, Hindu by culture and Sufi by persuasion, have come upon the myth of the birth of Hariputra, variously known as Harihara, Shashta, Ayyannar, or Ayyappa. Vishnu and Shiva (in the form of Mohini) coupled after the amrit manthan or Churning of the Oceans to issue a new god-child, Lord Ayyappa. In the temple at Thanjavur two priests ritually enact the copulation of the male gods, one cross-dressed as female with priests enacting the roles of the god's parents, Uma and Maheshwar, as they bless the marriage. In other Tamil Nadu temples the male priest cross-dresses to become Parvati to perform the linga abhishek or the ritual oblation to the linga. The mother-goddess chanting pre-Dravidian chants at Kerala's Theyyam is, of course, well known. The priest there wears a breastplate showing female breasts.

I also include the brother-love of Laxmana for Rama, the devotion of Hanuman for Rama, the love bond of friendship between Krishna and Balram and Krishna and Sudama from the Bhagvata Purana in this category of male bonding. The 'guru-shishya parampara' (tradition of discipleship with a teacher) had platonic love-overtones for both guru and shishya. Brotherly love, shorn of eroticism, was a form of male bonding in a world largely mistrustful of women. Mother-worship can lead as easily to homoerotic leanings as misogyny can; the two psychological states springing from the duality of the mother and the whore.

Much of Sanskrit writing celebrates love between man and woman. Man/man love could not be celebrated without offence to the audience. Hence much of the homosocial or the homoerotic content of Sanskrit texts has to be teased out of them by the alert or aware reader. Linguistic confusion and circumlocution was regularly practised in discussions of adolescent male awareness or mistrust of the female as in some tales of gender confusion in the Mahabharata.

In the medieval, largely Muslim Indian literary history, I include the Sufis who are bound each to each with bonds of love rather than sex. Woman, of course, is excluded from this world though there have been woman saints. Mir Taqi Mir's father was followed in the streets by a Sufi who when brought to the Delhi household of the Mir's became the young poet's teacher. So the teacher of both father and son was also their lover, giving the murshid-shagird silsila (student-teacher lineage) a new dimension. Rumi has said, 'To the sacred everything is sacred/To the profane everything is profane.' As every Sufi knows, the divine principle is male while the human soul is always female. Hence Rumi and Kabir are forced to speak as women while

Meerabai or Rabia of Basra can speak in their own gender. Traditionally, even in heterosexual Urdu poetry the love-object is always 'he'—a strategy of subterfuge—until the nineteenth-century Lucknow poets dared to introduce a woman as muse.

It was my city
but your alley:
I got lost

Searching you
In everyone's face.
I was mocked

Being innocent
you showed me your house

Being foolish
I lost my way

Quarrelling with others
didn't bring you back:
I only lost them

For the love I never had
I lost the loves I had

Cruel one!
if you remember me come home

Busy one
if you tire come home.

'It Was My City' by Mir Taki Mir (1722-1808)

In medieval Hindu India where the Chandelas built

Khajuraho and Tantra was at its height, bands of naked young men roamed the country from 'tirtha' to 'tirtha' trying to make their 'kundalinis' rise. You can still see such sadhus at the Kumbh Mela. The photographer Raghu Rai memorably caught one young sadhu with his penis wrapped around a walking stick for discipline. The medieval sadhus used little wood dildos (artificial penises) to make the psychic kundalini energy rise up the spine from the anal to the pineal region in the head.

In 1835, Macaulay with his Minute foisted Western education on India. A brown-skinned Englishman with English mind and manners was created. In the British presidencies of Bombay, Calcutta, Madras, the traditional family was under severe pressure for space—mental as well as physical. Women and children were crushed as men became schizophrenic culturally, wearing the veshti at home and the waistcoat at office. Homosexual children learnt schizophrenia at their convent schools. An imported suffering god-on-the-cross taught them sweet torment and self-guilt while in their 'pagan' playpens they were, well, happily 'pagan'. Homosexuality was fostered if not engendered and foisted upon children in single sex schools run by celibate teachers, usually priests. The work of the erstwhile gurukula was taken over by the Western missionaries.

The gurukulas enjoined an enforced twenty-five-year brahmacharya. Something was bound to happen within those sexually active first twenty-five years of a man's life. That something would be, out of necessity of circumstance in an all-male world, homosexuality, since woman was rigorously kept out of bounds. (Mahabharata, trans. Ganguly, 1897, pp. 968-73).

With the Bible came the Western narratives, Shakespeare, the novels of Dickens, Scott and Austen, the essays of Hazlitt and Lamb. My Parsi teacher at convent school told me I should never be marooned on an island without these four. How more marooned could I be than at school among heterosexual boys was beyond me. Not that these books within civilization spoke to my condition. They came severely disinfected and sanitized. The Old Testament was Moses but not Lot or Sodom or David who danced naked before the Ark. The New Testament was the Sermon on the Mount but not the Temptations of Christ. Shakespeare was *Romeo and Juliet* but not the sonnets. It was Shakespeare bowdlerized through Goan or Parsi schoolmarms' minds. (Bodies all of us did not have, only minds.)

In Calcutta the Charulatas sighed over Bankim's novels written a la Austen and the Brontes. They were all heterosexual. Adultery they had in plenty.

The novel form itself is Western. In a frenzy of post-colonialism today we are led to believe that the 'lok-katha' (or 'rupa-katha') and the 'burra katha' are the wellsprings of modern, Indian narratives. If so, how does one account for Tagore of *Ghare Baire*? For Jibanananda Das, the Ginsberg of fifties' Calcutta? It is almost a truism that Bankim is Scott. Aurobindo's brother, after all, was Wilde's confidant in London.

This is not to say that there are no local forms of narrative. The Ramlila of Delhi or the Nautanki of Uttar Pradesh are too well known to be elucidated here. The analogous Bengali form would be the 'burra katha', viz. the song of the heroes and their boons recounted at Durga Puja. These forms are used in the Hindi heartland even today in revamped versions. Just as the folk motifs on village walls of Bihar were transferred by Madhubani women onto rice paper to be sold in London, Nautanki was sanitized in *Teesri Kasam*, made memorable by Waheeda's dances in the Bombay film version. Kamleshwar's Hindi novel on homosexuality uses these folk forms.

Islam first came to south India in the eighth century AD. Kasargode, Mangalore, Calicut are largely Muslim today. The Mopilah is the descendant of Arab missionaries, traders, spice merchants, boat-builders. Quoilandi in

Malabar is famous for its gay boys even today. The dress
there is an Arab robe, thobba or djelebba in Arabic; jubba in
Arabized Malayalam. Malayalam is a ritualized language.
Even gay slang is elegant. 'Fellatio' is 'sucking the fruit',
'sodomy' is 'entry from behind' or 'unusual usual practice'
and so on. This is Mopilah slang. In Calicut homosexuality
is privately practised and publicly ridiculed. There is no
literature of, by or on homosexuals.

South Indian Brahminism practises taboos centred
around the menstruating woman. These taboos and fear of
pollution often turn the Iyengar and Iyer boys away from
women to other men. Homosexuality is not uncommon
among Brahmin boys in Tamil Nadu and Andhra. An elder
colleague, an Ayyangar, was compassionate to me: 'There,
but for the grace of God, go I!' Nowhere is homosexuality
proscribed in the shastras. There is no guilt. Nowhere is it
mentioned. The conspiracy of silence. Erasure. It does not
exist. No gay literature in Tamil or Telugu either. But the
Brahmin mind encompasses homosexuality and condones
it tacitly as one more illusion to be shed on the road to
Moksha. Artha and Kama were never proscribed, but
overindulgence is.

In Brahmin Karnataka the gurukulas surreptitiously
harboured homosexual teacher and students. Again, no
high brahminical literature on the subject. But the Dalits
have plays which refer to homosexual practices.
Unfortunately these texts are in local dialects which are
well-nigh untranslatable. As the gentrification of the
proletariat progresses apace, homosexuality will be pushed
further underground.

In Maharashtra, it could be poverty that forces the rural
farm labourer to Western tourists or city sahebs for sexual
favours tacitly exchanged for goods or cash. The big bad city
of Bombay and its money culture is never far away from any
village in Maharashtra. Rape of Dalit women and the
Yellamma culture are realities. The ethnographist, the late
Sontheimer lived with the male practitioners of the Vithoba

cult for a long time. He gave them draught cattle and bullocks for ploughing (a pair of bulls would cost as much as seven thousand rupees), he told me. These men-centred men held him in reverence as a saviour. Sai Paranjape's *Disha*, a film about migrant rural labour in the Bombay cotton mills, has a scene of homosexual overtures between Patekar and Yadav, the implication being that men-without-women practise occasional homosexuality in Bombay's labour-chawls as men do in prison or at sea. Mira Nair's *Salaam Bombay* had a severely abridged scene of homosexual horseplay between the drug-pushing Yadav and the film's child-hero. Actually these homeless children fear rape every night of their lives from the police, if not from older street people.

Bombay's films are not without its homoeroticism. The real love plot is again dosti or yaraana between the two heroes. The female lead is there only to lessen the homosexual sting. Women are for marriage, male friends for the love-emotion. It goes back to Mehboob's *Andaz*. Nargis comes between Raj and Dilip. She, a high society woman, marries Raj, murders Dilip and goes to jail in the Marxist Mehboob's melodrama. Interrogating modernity as well as capitalism, woman is the helpless victim in a male capitalist world. In Raj Kapoor's remake of it, *Sangam*, Raj loves Rajendra. Rajendra loves Raj's girl, Vyjayantimala. Rajendra has to commit suicide to resolve the love triangle. In *Sholay* it is the Amitabh-Dharmendra love story that is centre-stage. Illiterate street people, the bulk of India's film-going public hoot if Sanjay Dutt should sleep in his girlfriend's lap in *Naam*. They applaud when the boys are ready to die for each other, hunted down by the Hong Kong drug mafia or the police. These are the single-sex love myths alienated urban India lives by.

Modern India with its variety of languages is a challenge to any anthology editor. But homosexual writing in the vernacular addressing small-town audiences is non-explicit when available. There is the added difficulty in our society of social stigmatization of any contributor to a homosexual anthology. Tennessee Williams said just before his death that the modern homosexual faces not so much exploitation as loneliness. Ifti Nasim, Urdu poet, gender-bender, and ex-car salesman writes from the relative security of his Chicago penthouse about his exploited brethren in the subcontinent:

> The first stone was lifted by the mosque's preacher
> who had slept with me
> The second by the municipal councillor who had also
> slept with me

> —poem from *Narman (Man/Woman)*

Androgyny is a lonely business in any world. Those very men who sleep with us become our enemies in the very act of sex. Enemy, my enemy, I name you friend.

English speaking India yields strident new voices like Mahesh Dattani's or Raj Rao's, and there are mainstream writers of English-speaking India like Vikram Seth, writing on gay themes. From Urdu I include a homosexual-hating writer, Gyansingh Shatir, because like all peoples, the homosexuals have their share of scoundrels and child molesters. In high Marathi literature, Jnanpith-winning novelist Vishnu Khandekar's Yayati has captured the imagination of the homosexual painter Bhupen Khakhar of Baroda. Yayati talks of two brothers. One practises abstinence. When a woman comes to him, he tells her: 'Be for me a man.' The other brother, Yayati by name, is licentious. To regain his youth he couples with his own son and is regenerated. Bhupen Khakhar's painting with the same name shows a green Yayati with sagging scrotum beneath his pink-fleshed son who is also winged. So the gay painter has teased out a homoerotic myth from this allegory of conflict between kama and dharma.

Bhupen Khakhar who is Baroda based and well past his seventieth year is a painter in his prime. He is India's only openly gay painter. Younger artists—gay in private live, are still hiding for pecuniary benefits. A public that is paying high prices for art will not accept homosexuality. Bhupen has made his money as a chartered accountant and is free to paint as he likes. The homosexual British art critic Howard Hodgkins visits him regularly and is included in his anecdotal paintings a la Delacroix and Hockney.

Bhupen has now taken to prose in Gujarati. His stories satirize the mad craze for Western things of the moneyed Baroda bourgeoisie. 'If I wear lipstick will I be able to speak English?' asks one typical Gujarati lady in a Bhupen Khakhar story.

Every nation has a historic moment when it comes into its own and bursts upon the world's consciousness. Such a moment has already been defined by their literatures for India's women and Dalits. I am humbled to have been entrusted with defining the historic moment for India's homosexuals through their literature, old and new, heroic or pedestrian, lovely and lovelorn or rough and ironic.

What is remarkable is the number of genres homosexual writing encompasses and the easy transition from one genre to another in a single piece of work by taboo-breaking lives. Literature has no sex and poems have no sex organs. There is only good writing or bad writing. India's homosexuals have produced a lot of good writing, over the centuries a veritable feast. Here's a sampling. Enjoy!

July 1999   Hoshang Merchant

Public Meeting and Parting as Private Acts

Firaq Gorakhpuri

Look at your face in the mirror, friend
After our reunion it shines twice as bright

I am besotted with the scent of his words
His each word brings the scent of his lips

This isn't a public meeting since
My eyes are raised only to you

This coloured cloth hides a secret joy
There's current playing under the shroud of the grass

Loving grudgingly is no love, friend
Go! Now you have no sorrow from me

Nevertheless my life is spent
Either remembering or forgetting you

Your tearful shadow is the sorrow of the age
Before my sight plays this shadow eternally.

Translated by Hoshang Merchant

The Contract of Silence

Ashok Row Kavi

When the stirrings started, the fantasies were all very disturbing. Beautiful men floated in the mental mist, their pectorals and pubes making their sexuality all very obvious. And the bubble burst one day on the football grounds that were perched on the seashore of Mahim Bay.

Right there, in the middle of the game, everything came to a halt. The wolf-whistles were deafening. The girls had come into the ground for their recreation period while our game was still on. The boys loved it. That's the first time I realized that women were objects of sexual desire; an extraordinary feeling of something having gone wrong dawned on me. There were no women in my paradise.

It was nearly a year since my affair with S had started. He was a strapping, swarthy senior who was the object of my sexual desires. We had quick, furtive sex in the sprawling school campus. Sometimes it was the boys' cloakroom and sometimes behind the old banyan tree that grew in the grounds of the quaint one-storeyed structure that was the Bombay Scottish High School.

After a year of such bliss it was horrifying to be told that a chit of a girl was a better screw than I. I don't think I got over the wolf-whistles from S appreciating a top-heavy Anglo-Indian girl called Rosemary. 'What a juicy . . .' he had said. To me the female genitals were a sort of wound I had played doctor-doctor with (yes, with Rosemary's) and found too repulsive for words. How could anybody in his right mind think that it was juicy?

The decision that evening was a watershed in my life. I decided that I had to get to the bottom of this. Discussion with Anna (Daddy) was one way out. I was just over twelve. Anna was a barrel-chested film producer; sickeningly heterosexual, monogamous to a fault and an incredibly sensitive person. The discussion went along these lines:

Ashok: Anna, how are babies born?
Anna: Uh! What's the problem?
Ashok: The boys in school were discussing. They say that men and women do it like frogs. One-on-top-of-the-other. Is it true?
Anna: (Taking out a plug and socket from his electrical repair kit after much hesitation) It's more like this. When a plug gets into a socket, the electricity flows, you see. You see, men have the plugs and the women have the sockets. When they get together, things happen and the electricity flows. That's called sex.
Ashok: It sounds very unhygienic. How can they do that, it's too atrocious, Anna.

I felt completely betrayed. Even Anna thought it was right. To me it was not at all the natural way of things and nothing would convince me even if Anna thought it was the way things should be. I looked askance at him. My anxiety obviously made him uncomfortable.

Anna proved himself that day. He wasn't just a father. He was a friend. Next week, two volumes of Havelock Ellis's *The Psychology of Sex* were left conspicuously in the living-room. When I grabbed them, Anna groaned and heaved a sigh of relief. His job was over! Mine had just begun. What a journey that would be! I have yet to reach my destination.

Havelock Ellis was only the first step in exploring the

fascinating world I had been thrown into, as it were, by fate. Understanding one's sexuality is always a difficult and dreaded process on the path to adulthood. My steps into adulthood were even more difficult. My introverted nature, withdrawn to a fault sometimes, made talking out my problems a major hurdle. Coupled with this was my blunt way of asking questions which others found a bit unsettling.

Dr P, my psychiatrist, made the best of it! The early morning sessions with him at the Nair Hospital in Bombay intrigued my mother. I had to lie to her saying that they were part of my college routine. It was embarrassing the way Dr P handled my case: as if it were a deviation, an odd kind of behaviour which the rest of humanity didn't really like amidst it.

I was lucky in the fact that my homosexual identity was established as 'natural' before social regimentation could suppress it. Dr P took three sessions with me and then commented: 'You are all right. I am afraid I can do very little for you.' Of course, I was surprised when he thought fellatio (oral sex) was deviant. He got a psychiatric intern to sit in on one of my last sessions, who commented on my orientation till I burst out: 'I am afraid, Doctor, I am okay and you are deviant.' My visits to the venerable doctor ended on that friendly note.

It was then that I resolved to study my orientation as objectively as possible; this attitude helped me immensely in my career as a journalist. Though perfect objectivity is a myth, the effort to be objective is the hallmark of a professional journalist. But it is a quality that made it difficult for a person to operate in a profession swarming with ideological hacks of all kinds, as it was in the mid-eighties.

*

After high school it was college; from the tight discipline of Bombay Scottish it was to the scandalous open-mindedness of St. Xavier's. The first thing one noticed as a child of the Inquisition in Goa was the way we Hindus turned a Nelson's eye to blatantly bigoted minorities. The college, known for its alleged liberal education, was a clever Venus's fly-trap where 'modernization' was a synonym for Westernization.

Two incidents made me grow up very fast. V was a stunning woman of mixed parentage doing an arts course while I was in the science stream. It was V who took me under her wing and I learnt what it was to be a 'man'. Football and hockey took up most of my evenings while gossiping with V and M took up the recess time. Both women gave me the run-down on 'men' and I learnt to be the subversive in the male fraternity.

V is now a top banking official and is known for her savvy and ruthless ways with men. And yet the woman has never hurt anybody intentionally. 'You'll reap what you sow,' she used to repeat ad nauseam. Both girls were beautiful, buxom battleaxes whom men lusted after with frantic feverishness. All three of us would go to the Metro cinema nearby, bunking classes to catch the matinée shows at eleven in the morning. V and M discovered new ways to hassle men; like throwing empty popcorn bags filled with pee on the front rows and then pretending to be the paragons of virtue. They taught me how to lie with a straight face and face bullies head on.

A frightening incident took place on our visit to Elephanta. It taught me that men could always be cowed down by strong women. Our infamous trio (V, M and I) were taking a Sunday outing on the island of Elephanta in the Bombay harbour when I discovered that I was supposedly very privileged to have two girls with me. A bunch of boys started hassling us on our climb to the caves. It started with the line: '*Ai, battery. Do ladkion sey kya karte ho?*' (Hey spectac-wearing guy. What are you doing with two women?) Before it could get out of hand, V had gone up to the leader, caught him by the collar and given him a backhand whack. Meanwhile, M started a torrent of Punjabi abuse saying uncomplimentary things about their mothers. The boys took to their heels. That's when I learnt that men are essentially bullies and never stand up except in groups.

*

This would help me later on in the faction fighting in the gay community. The leanings of the 'society queens' in Bombay were mostly towards 'cadillac communism', as I cryptically called it. Tackling them was half the fun.

It started as the usual party gup-shup at K's place. The protagonist was a high-flying Oxbridge executive typical of the ruling political class: Mr A was an admirer of a proto-Pakistani columnist masquerading as a secularist, who was, in turn, a camp-follower of Ms Rana Kabbani, a Syrian feminist who appeared homophobic in her writings.

Ms Kabbani lashed out at the adventurer-Orientalists, like Sir Richard Burton and Lawrence of Arabia, for being 'deviants', read 'homosexuals'. Ms Kabbani's grouse was that these 'deviants' had been rather callous about the alleged 'unbridled sexuality' of the Orient; it reflected their own sexual orientation. Mr A accepted this vapid anti-Occidentalism and homophobia. But A did not challenge the fact that both pederasty and paedophilia were inherent to Arab cultures.

In fact, Kabbani herself in her 'research' refuses to even acknowledge the high tension male-male sexuality present in Arab/Muslim cultures.

It was K, the host, who tried to bring all the factions together whereas the cadillac-communist brigade never let that hinder their tirade against *Bombay Dost*.[*] This conversation should suffice.

---

[*] *Bombay Dost* is the first magazine for homosexuals to be published in India. It was founded in 1990 by Ashok Row Kavi.

Ashok: We need a lesbian and gay newsletter now.

Cadillac-communist(CC): But why? There are more urgent priorities. Like the poor in India; eliminating poverty is first priority. We homos are doing quite well, thank you.

Ashok: Sure you're doing well in your Gymkhana where you suck off the chokra-boys and pay them off. But what about the guys out there who need support networks?

CC: Who needs those vernacular creeps? They are just good for bad fucks!

Ashok: Oh really . . . That is terrific commitment towards democracy and equality.

CC: Look, if I want to show solidarity I do it at the India Day Parade in New York. I was there in my sari-drag last year. Here it's different.

Ashok: Why?

CC: Gay Lib is no priority here. Remember that dialogue from *Chakra* where the hero says: *Pehle pet ka sawal aur phir pet ke nichey ka sawal* (First consider the matters concerning your stomach and then think about what is below your stomach: meaning sexuality).

Ashok: And who is to determine this priority?

CC: The party leadership, of course. You will have to be educated for this, you know.

Ashok: So the party [in this case the Communist Party (Marxist)] will tell us how large a slice of cake we can have of freedom? But they say it is a bourgeoise decadence. So . . .

CC: The party will decide someday that it is not.

Ashok: What do we do in the meantime, arsehole? Vegetate and grow our cherries back, you prick!

CC: Oh dear, don't start your abuses.

That was the beginning of a long and bitter war within the gay community which I won hands down. And it was thanks to V and her ways that I had learnt to tackle this sinecure class.

The argument in K's house was interesting in the sense that it exposed the arrogance of India's ruling class. It was K, a systems manager in one of the world's largest multinationals, who created space for *Bombay Dost* in his company house.

*

Coming out to V and M was an uneasy experience though it taught me that if people really loved you, they wouldn't care about your sexuality. When V decided to explore what sexual possibilities existed between us, it was a disaster. She dismissed the whole episode with the line: 'Ashok, I always knew it but that's what makes you what you are: a gentle understanding guy!' It was the most touching thing V had done for a long time. After that we grew closer than ever before.

It was around that time that Khushwant Singh took over the *Illustrated Weekly of India*, then India's premier periodical. I was barely eighteen but the subject kept cropping up in my mind. How was it possible to reach out to a scattered, invisible community? I thought it was best to write about the history of homosexuality in Europe and then connect it up with the scene in India.

Surprisingly, Khushwant published the article. I received over 350 letters and that got me entry into an incredible gay circuit. B was a top advertising executive who ran an 'illegal' gay bar in his digs on Marine Drive. B would start slapping on make-up at four in the afternoon. He would then traipse over to Chowpatty to pick up a malishwala (masseur). B had one kink—his dressing-table had a small collection of injection vials filled with yellow-coloured liquid. B's kink was collecting the pee of all his 'tricks' (the men he slept with). It was weird to see those vials resting cheek by jowl with Elizabeth Arden and Christian Dior. But a big battle was on the cards.

The usual procedure at B's bar was to get your own bottle and keep it in the cabinet. The servant measured out the drinks and marked the level with a wax pencil. Soon, Tony (my boss) and I discovered that we never felt even a bit high despite three stiff pegs. Guess what? B used to drain our bottles and pour in doctored gin. Tony was so furious that he threw the pee-collection on to the roof of Talk-of-the-Town, the restaurant directly below the apartment. We have called the place 'Pee-of-the-Town' since then. As for B, he sat down in front of his opulent dressing-table with tears streaming down his face, making deep furrows in the Max Factor. 'Oh dear, dear me, I'll have to collect their pee all over again,' he screeched in a high soprano.

That was the next lesson: never be taken for granted in the gay world or they'll take advantage of you. B was such a selfish bitch that when he got into trouble, all his friends deserted him and he died on the pavement outside Stev George Hospital in downtown Bombay.

*

Tony started *Debonair* as a lark. The owner, Susheel Somani, was one of those rich industrialists who liked what is called 'social-gup-shup' (society gossip) and Tony was very good at it. He taught me how male models needed to have kerchieves wrapped round their penises to make their crotches look gargantuan, most of them being rather small in that department. We used to leave the selection of the woman for the centrespread to Moinuddin, our technical director, while we concentrated on the main readership of *Debonair*—MEN.

Tony taught me how shallow sophistication was. He pulled off some pretty silly capers in a south Bombay bar which used to be a great cruising place in those days when pink gins were just five chips. But he also taught me something else; you never get men through perseverance. Manipulation and constantly shifting grounds were the war zones of the sexual battles between men and men. It was amazing how petty and puerile men could be. In many cases, I discovered that men could be more bitchy and gossipy than women. In most cases, gays always had the upper hand. It was precisely for that reason that heterosexual men feared homos. Insecure women, not very confident of their sexuality, were the other enemies of gay men. But that was again brought home to me in an incident at work.

Ms A was a top-heavy woman reporter transferred from the Delhi office to the *Indian Express* in Bombay. She was an instant hit with my seniors—R and his coterie. Soon she was playing one person off against another with transparent sexuality. One day, she tried the 'let-my-palloo-fall-so-you-can-see-my-cleavage' with me and it failed. When she heard about my being gay, she lost her shirt. We were enemies from that instant and I saw the ancient evil one in her eye; the curse of a woman rejected! There is nothing more contemptible and homophobic than a woman who uses her sexuality to advance her cause. And homosexuals through history have known exactly such women and used them to advantage. The way Alexander used his Persian queen and his mother to conquer the world is a reminder of gay men's understanding of insecure women.

*

However, it was discovering India's homosexual heritage that made the most sense to me. By now, it was obvious that formal education was not worth the paper the degrees were printed on. India's educational infrastructure was built by Macaulay to stuff a shelf full of books and overload a child's neurons. A general deterioration was so obvious in the intellectual discussions one went to that it was undignified to argue with some of the leftist hacks. The general tendency was to defend the minorities regardless of what they did. For example, the defence of the government's reservation policy was too foolish for words. Just because a certain class or caste made up twenty per cent of the populace it was promised twenty per cent of the jobs. This Mandalization of Indian society was an extraordinary divisive method taking the reservation policy to ridiculous lengths. But that was exactly the intention of this ruling class.

I argued otherwise. If gays were ten per cent of the economically active population, did that mean that we deserved only ten per cent of the jobs in the IAS? That was ridiculous because we might have ninety per cent of the creative jobs in advertising, for example, or we might have all the jobs in the starry film world and on the stage. The world's homosexual minority had learnt through the ages not to be marginalized. Gays everywhere had a lesson to teach other minorities on how not to be disempowered. Studying religion helped. It came with a bang one day even as my second love affair was coming to a stormy end. My 'mother-in-law', a Muslim, did everything but burn me for dowry, as I sarcastically recall now on hindsight. But the worst complaint she had had was that I had turned her sonny boy's bedroom into a 'butkhana' (den of idols). However much I endeavoured to satisfy her, the religious question always came foremost. Finally, the relationship floundered on the reef of religion and broke up. I never looked back. I was grateful for the memories and decided that there was no room for bitterness. M, from a feudal Muslim family, still regrets it and thinks it would have worked if his mother hadn't interfered, something impossible to achieve in India.

*

My knowledge of Islam would come in handy when I faced TV cameras on Channel Four in England. The chief mullah of a London mosque pitched Leviticus at us ('thou shall not sleep with a man as thou sleeps with a woman') and the gay group had its snappy answer ready. 'We don't sleep with men as we sleep with women. We sleep with men as we should sleep with men.' That stumped the mullah.

When I insisted that the Prophet was a benevolent and broad-minded soul, the mullah brought out a book which he waved about. 'This book names a hundred diseases which homosexuals carry. They are disease carriers,' he ranted. I quickly brought out my filofax and waved it. 'I've got a book which shows that heterosexuals carry five hundred diseases,' I retorted. That left him foaming at the mouth. The trick with religious bigots is to fight them on their own territory.

If Islam in India curbed the open sexuality of feminine eroticism—notice the disfigured Hindu temple sculptures—male homosexuality was brought out of the closet almost immediately by the Mughal emperor Babar, who built the great gardens at Agra for the Afghani man he loved. This great love affair was commented on wryly by his daughter, Gulbadan, in her autobiography spanning the lives of four Mughal emperors.

*

I had managed to rediscover much of my Hindu heritage with a stint at the Ramakrishna Mission where Swami Ganeshananda and Swami Harshananda, two extraordinary monks, managed to bestow on me the strict regimen of a monastic asceticism. Even amidst plenty, I never again felt the urge to join the rat race for the dazzling consumer materialism that epitomizes the middle class in India. It also gave me great strength during my poverty-stricken days when I was trying to put Bombay Dost on its feet and money was difficult to come by.

It was one of these two monks who first 'unveiled' my homosexuality through scribblings in a notebook in which scriptural questions were to be answered. I was called immediately into his study. The counselling session went like this:

Swamiji: Ashok, this is a very interesting side of your personality. Are you here to study about the spirit or are you running away from some torment of your flesh? [I just loved that line.]

Ashok: Swamiji, I really don't know. But I must tell you that I have some very puzzling dreams . . .

Swamiji: Puzzling dreams? What does that mean?

Ashok: Confusing in the sense that I dream of men instead of women. I feel that is wrong . . . don't you think so?

Swamiji: No, I don't think that is wrong at all. Why do you feel so bad about it? Do you feel it is wrong?

Ashok: No, I don't feel it is wrong but I've been made to think so.

Swamiji: By whom? Why?

Ashok: By society; people around me. Because what I want to do is considered wrong.

Swamiji: Look, what is wrong is relative. I don't think many rules made by man would be liked by God. They were written by men for men. Just as an example: it is considered good manners among Eskimos to offer their wives to strangers as a gesture of goodwill but it is wrong in most other cultures. Now, can we call the Eskimos uncivilized because of that? Don't get taken in by what others say is right or wrong. Drag everything deep into your heart, study it with discrimination and then ask the question—am I hurting any soul through my action? Can the pain be avoided and if so for what goal? Is the goal worth achieving? When you get sound answers for those questions then go ahead and do it, boldly and brazenly. Be like Swamiji [Vivekananda] and stop not till the goal is reached.

Ashok: But what about people? They can be very cruel . . .

Swamiji: But the world has always been a cruel place, Ashok. Whatever makes you think that a python eats its prey with love or compassion? In more ways than one, even Thakur [Shri Ramakrishna] said that 'a cobra worships you with his venom because it is the only precious thing he has'. [This was when one disciple told Shri Ramakrishna that another disciple used to go to Calcutta and spread nasty stories about him.] So don't worry about the world. Try to make a reasonable life for yourself by not hurting anybody as far as possible. When you go out and find somebody purposely and wilfully obstructing you or hurting you then cut him down dead. Don't pussyfoot with him. Better a clean kill than a half-dead snake who might bite you when you are unaware.

Ashok: But I think I am a homosexual . . .

Swamiji: Look, you might be one. Even if you are, so what? Men have loved each other since the beginning of mankind. You are not someone with horns. Try and sort that out using those three questions I told you to answer. If the answers satisfy you then go ahead and make a life for yourself and fight for what you think is right. But remember then what is good for you should be good for all who think like you. It cannot be only right for you, and your right to happiness must mean the least unhappiness for others around you. Finally, when you have lived out your life according to those beliefs, there is a place to rest. That is what this ashram is about. It is not a place to run away to. Not a place to discover God by running away from life. Life is like the coconut tree which slowly sheds its leaves and then bears fruit when it grows tall and looks from high above upon the earth below. . .

Ashok: Swamiji, if only things were as easy as you make them sound . . .

Swamiji: Life is very easy if you have your priorities right. Go out there and act. Action makes the man. Don't be like other Hindus. We fools never 'act'. We pass the buck, we preach and pontificate about our great philosophy, the most elevating on earth . . . Because Hindus never 'act', that is one quality Vivekananda lauded in the Western civilization. Through 'action' comes creation. Vishnu conquers infinite Time 'Kala' [the great hooded cobra on which he is shown sitting] but only when he summons Brahma [the creator] does the Universe and mankind come into being. Otherwise who would have been there to admire Him? So just go out there and start doing things. And do them to the best of your capability.

This conversation, which I had noted in my diary, has been reproduced as best as possible. Much of it was in the vernacular (Marathi and Konkani) and some of those colloquial nuances have been lost. But it was in a monastery that my 'coming out' took place. I am ever grateful to the monks of the Ramakrishna order for making my coming out so painless and worthy of all that is great in man's heritage. Thank you, Swamiji! It is finally only people like you who will be heard and admired for what you are; a truly evolved human being.

*

My coming out was with a bang. When I returned home I would go out to cruise with a vengeance. Since my first days in the *Indian Express* as a junior reporter, rarely, if ever, did I come home before midnight. And the scores? For people who don't know what gay life is, Bombay can be a dead place after nine at night. For us gays, life began after sunset. From Chowpatty; the famous beach in the centre of town where the popular bhelpuri was invented, all the way to Borivili where even the guards at the National Park were gay.

My coming out, to office colleagues, was dramatic. Most of us reporters and sub-editors took the last train home from Churchgate in South Bombay. The last train at 1 a.m. was also called the Queen's Special in gay slang. There were five of us led by R, an orthodox Karnataka linguist who believed even heterosexuality was sinful. That Saturday night there was a particularly heated argument about sex. It went like this:

R [my senior]: I'm sick of this sex, sex, sex all the time in our magazine section. Why don't they stop talking about it? It's sick!
Ashok: What's so sick about it? It's a subject that is worth discussing in a repressive society . . .
R: Well, it's embarrassing. It's . . .

Into the railway coach walked M, a particularly glamorous glitterbug of a gay. He was dressed to kill; there was stardust in his hair and on his face and he was wearing a tanktop, showing off his biceps and pectorals to good effect.

M: Oh, you silly fellow. Where were you tonight? Do you know the fun we had at the Bandstand? [He was talking of the Cooperage Bandstand where gays cruised navy boys.]

Ashok: [trying to fob off conversing with M] Oh M. Sorry, but I was working. This is my boss at the office. [This was supposed to be a hint to M to shut up but it wasn't taken.]

M: The seafood [navy guys] was fantastic, yaar. I got this Rajput fellow who went on and on in Lovelane [a little alley behind the Bandstand]. I got him through the fence man. I still have the chain-link marks on my bum yaar. Yum, yum!

I was blushing. R was red as a lobster in a steampot. Finally R got up and heaved out of the compartment at Marine Lines. My cover was blown by M who went on chattering about his conquests.

But, to R's credit, the subject never came up again. In spite of being such a conservative fellow, his attitude never changed nor has he made a single homophobic remark to date. R refuses to even acknowledge my sexuality and there it stands.

*

It was by looking at Akka's condition that I knew my position as a single person was a severe handicap in India. Akka was Anna's only and elder sister. She was also a child-widow and had come to live with us when she lost her husband at sixteen. Though respected and loved as the head of our family, even as a surrogate mother to us, her position was secure only on a contract—the contract of silence; silence about her sexuality.

This was my position too. I was secure in my position as the patriarch of the Row-Kavis, being the eldest, unmarried brahmachari (bachelor) brother. But this security was tied to a silence regarding my sexuality. Any sexuality, if not harnessed for the family good, was taboo. I would finally break that silence to transgress the social contract that holds homosexuals and lesbians prisoners of a heterosexist society. This I was, I think, fated to do. It was part of my secular mission and the result of my liberation at the Ramakrishna monastery. I am grateful to the monks for the spiritual strength they gave me. It would give me a firm commitment in seeing that *Bombay Dost* would succeed.

Akka's final isolation and rejection by every child she raised would convince me that Indian families held nothing sacred in their drive for self-perpetration. Towards the end, at seventy-four, she would be a bitter but brave old woman. The child she had rejected because it was weak and had few chances of survival had grown up to be a homosexual, a social outcast. The first category she did not understand, the second she had fought all her life to avoid becoming a part of. But her silence had not paid off. The sacrifice she had made—of her sexuality—in order to bring up her brother's children had been taken for granted. She discovered that she had nothing to call her own.

I decided never to let that happen to me. The family—and the world—had to accept Ashok Row Kavi, complete with his homosexuality. Or nothing at all. Those who chose the second option would get the right retort: a cold rejection! On that score there could be no compromise.

*

Bombay in the seventies and early eighties was ripe for a gay sub-culture. A distinct class of skilled professionals had a firm grip on the city's cultural life. A corporate work ethic had finally evolved in contrast to the babu-raj of Delhi and the Bengali queasiness regarding sexuality in Calcutta. All these signs were important ingredients for a gay sub-culture.

There were already rather naughty gay parties in such staid places like Matunga and Ghatkopar. I went for a gay party hosted in a Marathi school in Mulund where a teacher's housing quarters had been turned into an orgy room. Within five years, the private feature of these gay parties had gone public. The first such leap forward was thanks to a crazy incident at an ace Indian Air Force (IAF) pilot's house on Pali Hill.

B, the pilot, had left the IAF thanks to a liaison between him and the mess cook that was about to burst into the open. If B had stayed on in the IAF, he would possibly have been not merely the most handsome officer in the 'Vayu Sena' but also the Chief of Air Staff. However, they allowed him an honourable discharge if he resigned his commission. He left gladly to join up as the head of an agricultural air-spraying business.

We were having an innocent orgy in his bedroom while his wife was supposedly away in Calcutta or wherever. The bed had been removed and wall-to-wall mattresses had been laid out with rubber matting covering them. Anybody going into the room was to remove his clothes and throw them on clothes-horses placed outside the door. After six men had trooped in bare-assed, a can of coconut oil was poured over the human pyramid. It was fun except that I'd never liked group sex. It turned into a nightmare when the lights suddenly came on and B's wife stood at the door screaming like a banshee. Her husband had his legs in the air (we called it the Flying Angel position) being screwed by a stud from Thane. I've never seen such an olympic race to get out of a house.

Anyway, I decided that enough was enough and soon after that we had Bombay's first mad public party at a hotel in suburban Ghatkopar. The owner had decorated the whole terrace with twinkling lights and we had numbered tickets with tight security. Each ticket had to be sold against two guarantees from established gays.

It was amazing to see the energy liberated that day. Gay couples like R and V thought it was the first time they could show their love for each other. Snazzy singles like C and F flirted madly. And the prizes for individual dances like mujra musicals and rumba-sambas were snapped up by unexpected queens from the suburbs. It was a grand exposition of talent, such as had never been seen before, all in one place. Queens came dressed to kill, some in exaggerated macho clothes while others wore feathers and sequins. Glitter powder, silver lipstick and high-heeled shoes, all the things Ghatkopar had never seen before. As for the 'hotel', some of the waiters did get seduced but it was not the gays who were at fault. After all, the beautiful and the bold could hardly be blamed for what they were, mad crazy poofs.

Nothing succeeds like excess, goes the saying. And soon R from Chembur, an orthodox little South Indian Brahmin, started organizing the first gay do's. By then, in April 1990, the first copy of *Bombay Dost* had hit the city like a ton of bricks. We got excellent coverage.

The first issue was historic in more ways than one. First, the Editorial Collective of *Bombay Dost* stumped quite a few from the cadillac-communist brigade. The alleged hard core Rashtriya Swayamsevak Sanghi, me of course, had inducted three Muslim male members into the Collective. Out of the three women, one was a Muslim. So if there was a divide along communal lines, I would be out-voted.

Efforts to torpedo the venture started immediately. The main opposition faction was led by a film director who thought he ought to be leading the movement.

It got to be ridiculous, actually. They started with a call to socially boycott me. Then a graduate of the IIM, Ahmedabad, got into a crazy, drunken, verbal assault on me even as he asked me in a hushed voice: 'As one Brahmin to another, tell me, how can you work with Muslims?' This from an avowed secularist!

Bombay Dost went from strength to strength. We were reported in the *New York Times*, the *London Times* and even in the esoteric Columbia School of Journalism's magazine.

By the fifth issue, *Bombay Dost* had started getting

advertisements which had an immediate impact. It was amazing how nobody had seen this huge niche market; fifty million males waiting for just such a newsletter. *Bombay Dost* was not just a newsletter but a movement by now. It was nearly a year since we had started off as an underground sheet for the gay and lesbian community but it represented something much more. *Bombay Dost* was a lifeboat for many people who thought they had no one to turn to. In a heterosexist world where marriage was a marketplace, we had created a space to be ourselves. But there was trouble in paradise!

When we had started we hadn't expected the type of response we got which changed our agenda. We had just managed to get a pokey little space in a business centre at Bandra, opposite the station. It was to be commented upon nastily by Arvind Kala, who wrote a book on homosexuals in India.

One day, after the first issue had been out for a month, there was a desperate call from Mrs Pinto, the manager of the business centre we were using as our mail-in address.

'Why is nobody picking up the mail,' she asked tiredly. 'We have 200 letters here. For heavens' sake somebody had better come and pick it up,' she added.

The torrent had started! Those first letters were like winged messengers from my huge new family spread over the subcontinent. Many were practising homosexuals who had not evolved a self-identity. India's gays were like swans swimming in a dream waiting for that magic touch to wake them up.

But there were some who disagreed—mostly English-educated Indians with a skin-deep knowledge of not just their own culture but also of what was happening abroad; this lot were mostly armchair critics. But some of them felt that it was too soon to have a Gay Consciousness Movement. The regional and vernacular press had lurid stories of how *Dost* had horrendous male nudes and pornography. Most of these stories were, of course, untrue, but the best one was an interview a local politician gave in which a new theory of homosexuality was propounded. According to him, homos were dangerous because they seduced young boys. Also the cause of homosexuality 'was a blood disorder where female blood corpuscles ate up the male blood corpuscles and a man's masculinity was subverted by terrible female characteristics'. It showed a distinct link between homophobia and misogyny.

However, it was within the home that much of the bitterness bore fruit. One of my siblings complained to Amma (Mother) that his eldest brother's homosexuality was making life miserable for his poor dear wife and two kids. The wife mostly ate out while the kids were left with the ayah to turn into ill-bred brats. It was strange that his wife's activities (questionable to say the least but which I shall not expand on) were not reflecting on the kids.

Amma stood up bravely to the age-old trick. Suggested Amma when it was brought to her notice, 'Look, this duo is the typical modern lot. They want to have their cake and eat it. My suggestion is that he·should give up the Row-Kavi surname and take up his wife's surname. If he used his elder brother's name when it suited him, he can't turn around and try disowning him now. In fact, I'm ready to disown him.'

Sure enough, when Akka died in March 1993, and I was away in Canada, Amma saw to it that that particular sibling was refused permission to touch the funeral fire and the aasti (ashes) of the old lady. He had been disowned in public, a fitting reply to him and his painted, homophobic wife.

My poor little brother with his perpetual pout had committed the other cardinal sin that gays love to watch out for: assume too many things in a war they thought would be fought for money. Little do heterosexuals know that money is the last thing on a gay mind when a serious war begins.

Probably, V's lessons had been learnt extra well by me. Though avoiding confrontation and conflict is the best way out for gays who have suffered through the centuries for their sexual orientation, I think gays make excellent fighters when the situation demands it. Playing the game of reconciliation and yet being prepared for confrontation have been the watchwords of this community as the careful management of our family squabbles had showed.

*

Bombay Dost progressed by leaps and bounds. Far too much responsibility fell on me and bearing the cross was no cakewalk.

By December 1991, I was already on the verge of a breakdown. But so crucial was the work and so critical the situation that there was no way that events could be slowed down for my sake. As Rebecca Savila, present secretary-general of the International Lesbian and Gay Association, would keep repeating: 'The planet's oldest and most persecuted minority now faces a now-or-never chance. We either learn to fight for dignity, demanding nothing more than what should be every world citizen's right or we fight to get this invisible nation together.'

As many of us Asian gay activists had carefully confided to our government health officials, the conclusion by the World Health Organisation (WHO) that the spread of HIV/AIDS in Asia was heterosexual was wrong. Not only was HIV/AIDS detected in India by forcibly testing female prostitutes but it pretended that homosexuality just did not exist.

The incursion of Western ideas through Christianity and communism had wiped out the very visibility of sexual minorities. So thoroughly had this been achieved that most Indians were ashamed of the homosexual heritage within Indian culture. The great god at the Sabarimalai shrine in Kerala, Ayyappa-Skanda, was not only a product of a sexual union between Shiva and Vishnu but he was called the husband of all army-men. In the Renuka-Yellamma tradition, boys too would be dedicated to the fertility goddess. But this found no mention in the concocted histories or mythologies.

Now, of course, all these and more would have to be harnessed to fight the new scourge of mankind, HIV / AIDS. The Panos Institute in London had already noted something new happening in Asia. In its November 1991 issue of *WorldAIDS Briefing*, the premier Institute reporting the new frightening disease, had called homosexuals 'The Unsung Heroes in the South'.

WorldAIDS Briefing put it bluntly: 'Despite formidable proscriptions against homosexuality in many developing countries and Eastern Europe, gay (homosexual) men have been an advance guard of AIDS educators and carers.' It quoted *Bombay Dost* extensively, forcing the Indian health authorities to take us seriously.

The only way out was continued education and a simultaneous campaign to sensitize Asian homosexuals to consolidate their identity. In Kuala Lumpur, my friend Heesham Hussein and in Indonesia, Dede Oetamo would also feel the same way. We linked up with the Filipino gay activist, Jomar of Reachout and Austero Bong of the Library Foundation, Roy Chan representing Singapore's gay groups and finally, the elderly Minami-San of Japan to set up the Gay Asian and Lesbians Groups' Association (GALGA). GALGA, set up in late 1992, was the first umbrella organization of Asian gay groups to help the new invisible minorities all over Asia. Sexually abused and suppressed by the heterosexist majority, Asia's myriad lesbian and gay groups hoped to lead their flocks into a more dignified lifestyle in a future rampant with AIDS and other killer Sexually Transmitted Diseases.

Mid-1992 was really one of the most hectic periods of my life. Starting with a workshop for US Congressmen in Washington I did an exhausting tour of six cities in three countries. After presenting a paper on the 'Emerging gay peer groups in Bombay' at Amsterdam's Eighth International Congress on HIV/AIDS, I came home to burnout and bad news: I had diabetes and drug-resistant tuberculosis.

Lying in my hospital bed, dejected and depressed, there was no time to wallow in self-pity. My friends never left me alone! The nurse would say, 'Your family may have forgotten you but you sure have a lot of friends.'

There was Suhail and Shridhar and Ramesh, Salim, Edwin in drag and podgy, ageing Chandan and studious Yusuf and Jehangir and Sopan and Cory, Rakesh and Pallav; every day! They came with flowers and naughty, nasty get-well cards ('You'll do ANYTHING to get attention, won't you,' screeched one). The nurses had a problem driving them out after visiting hours. One even gave a rude nurse a few tips on making up her face!

I had come home!

Shivraj

Kamleshwar

There were many stories current about him. He had come to the town four years ago, on a full moon night. Sadhus, sanyasis and yogis adept in tantric lore were a common sight in the bazaars of the town. One such mahatma expatiated more on the importance of the town than on God and was keen to build an ashram there.

Many years ago, they had seen him going about the town in the evenings. 'I've taken a vow to go on a pilgrimage to Badridham,' he would proclaim. 'One maund of flour, ten seers of ghee, twenty seers of rice and five hundred rupees—that's all I need. I seek Krishna Maharaj's benevolence.' He would go from one lane to another, ringing a bell. No one ever saw him receiving alms. But it was said that he had been able to fulfil his vow and Sarvanandji—for that was his name—left on a pilgrimage to Badridham.

Before he left, he managed to build a small hermitage in a lonely spot on the outskirts of the town and installed an idol of one of the thirty-three lakh gods in it. He had also planted a peepul sapling outside his hermitage. People looked at it in wonder. 'It's a miracle!' they said. A barren patch of land, where even a cactus plant would not grow, now had a peepul tree.

God was indeed kind to Sarvanand and soon his fame spread throughout the district. It was said that he had just to stand with his hand lifted towards the sky and miracles would happen. It was through his blessing that Jai Kishan, the sweetmeat seller, got the gift of a son in his old age. He had married four times but none of his wives obliged him with a child to carry on the family lineage. But the fourth wife, at long last, fulfilled his wishes. Sarvanand became famous overnight. Jai Kishan's wife expressed a desire to have Sarvanandji as her guru and devote the rest of her life to serving him as a dasi. Sarvanandji readily acceded to her wishes. Jai Kishan's wife was grateful. But didn't all sadhus regard woman as the root of all sins? Soon that root of sins became so fertile that it bore fruit every year. Jai Kishan was impressed. He entrusted his shop to his servant's care, shaved his head and became the mahatma's devotee. Then he went on a fund-raising mission for a sadhu ashram upon which Sarvanand had set his heart. Ten years later, on a full moon night, the ashram was inaugurated to the chanting of sacred mantras. From then on, it became an annual practice to have a religious congregation on that auspicious day. Holy men from distant places came to attend the function.

Four years ago, a big religious function was held at the ashram for which preparations had started a month in advance. By now twenty sadhus were permanently residing there. Sarvanand had adopted four disciples and started a religious sect of his own. One of the disciples was a Brahmin and the other three were sons of sweetmeat sellers.

To collect funds and foodgrains for the function the sadhus from the ashram had swarmed over the whole area like locusts. The devotees dedicated their vagabond sons to the ashram and put them under Sarvanand's tutelage.

Shivraj's case, however, was different. His father had asked Shivraj to touch Sarvanand's feet and then said to him in all humility, 'Maharaj, his salvation lies at your feet. How can he find it in a house of sinners like us? Maharaj, let him acquire wisdom at your feet. Teach him Sanskrit, teach him the Vedas and the Shastras . . .'

Shivraj was thirteen years old at that time. Swamiji brought him to the ashram with him. There were thirty other boys there who looked at one another like frightened deer. They were called upon to take to the life of brahmacharya. They were to renounce cereals for a month in advance of the date of initiation, and then were administered the vow.

A new life began for Shivraj. His head was shaved, leaving a thick tuft over his scalp. He wore wooden sandals and saffron-coloured clothes. A sandalpaste mark was painted over his face from the tip of his nose to his forehead and he was asked to observe silence for a full month.

Boundless are the benedictions of the Ramayana. The young novitiates who had taken a vow of silence communicated with each other in couplets from the holy book. When caught, they were forced to repeat the Gayatri mantra twenty times in their hearts. Most of them were Brahmin boys and had never thought that life at the ashram would be so easy. In the early hours they chanted mantras from the Vedas and then did Surya Namaskar (obeisance to the sun). In the afternoon they recited from the *Gita* and in the evening sang hymns to the accompaniment of music. This was their daily ritual after the month of silence was over.

When the hymns were sung the brahmacharis were seated in the front row. Behind them sat the devotees. One day when the kirtan was in full swing and the harmonium and the drum were at their loudest, Swami Gyananand went into a trance and started dancing before the idol. Rangeelay was so moved that he also started dancing and fell down in a swoon. The congregation, which was swaying in tune with the hymns, was astounded. The kirtan stopped and they all gathered round the prostrate Rangeelay. Rangeelay was a god! The chosen one! How did it matter that he was illiterate? God resides in every heart. One of the devotees made the sacred sandalpaste mark on Rangeelay's forehead. 'That's how the mortal bird flies to his god!' he said. 'Many such instances are quoted in our scriptures. Who wouldn't aspire for such a blessed end?'

Swamiji was informed. He came out of his hermitage

muttering, 'Hare Ram, Hare Krishna!' He was so overwhelmed that tears came to his eyes. 'O God! Great are your ways,' he mumbled and then announced that Rangeelay was more exalted than he was, for to go into a swoon was the first step to salvation. Rangeelay, he said, had acquired the divine power of snapping the ties between the body and the soul.

Shivraj, who was standing by, was asked to bring water to sprinkle over Rangeelay's face. Sarnam Singh took the vessel from Shivraj and after observing the proper ritual so as to invoke the right spirits, sprinkled the water over Rangeelay's face. He poured one full lota over him but Rangeelay's jaws remained locked. A few more mantras were mumbled. Rangeelay opened his eyes and stared at Shivraj. He caught hold of his legs and started writhing before him. 'He's very much like what I saw,' he moaned.

Rangeelay would not let go of Shivraj's legs. 'Give me salvation,' he moaned again and again. 'I'm lying at your divine feet.' Scared, Shivraj tried to withdraw his feet. It was after many minutes that Rangeelay returned to the material world.

'He resembled Shivraj a great deal,' Rangeelay explained to Sarnam Singh and others while returning to the bus stand at midnight. 'He had a bow and arrow in his hand and a crown upon his head. Oh, what effulgence! I was blinded by its dazzle. He was everywhere, brother.' Rangeelay firmly gripped Sarnam Singh's arm. 'And how still everything was! A light shone in my heart. It was God Himself standing before me. I don't know what happened afterwards. Why did you bring me out of that trance, brother? Why were you so cruel to me, brother?'

From that day Shivraj among the brahmcharis and Rangeelay among the devotees, became marked persons and their prestige rose. God had entered them, making their bodies pure. People would stop Rangeelay on the road and question him about his experience.

'It is the way Bharat Mata has entered Subhash Babu's

body,' Rangeelay explained. 'No doubt he was a loyal subject of the great Empress Victoria. But he could not close his ears to the call of the motherland. You see, the Empress could not take the place of the motherland. Subhash Babu went from place to place, incognito. He roamed the jungles and then lit the divine fire which brought freedom to our country. It was through his benediction that Gandhi Baba and Nehruji held the reins of the country.'

He stared into space. 'I'm also ordained to move about incognito and light the divine fire,' he said, putting on a grave expression.

'What for?' the betel seller asked.

Rangeelay gave him a mysterious smile and rose to his feet.

Everyday Rangeelay took some money from Sarnam Singh and bought fruit for Shivraj. For three or four days Shivraj accepted the fruits and made them over to the common mess. But later, Rangeelay's manners began to irk him. He would make Shivraj sit by his side and bore him with his talk. 'How soft your hands are! Your parents are indeed lucky to have such a promising son. Come with me some day. I'll take you round the bazaar.'

Shivraj would keep nodding, for he had taken a vow of silence. One day, one of his companions reported to Swamiji that Shivraj was not true to his vow. From that day onwards Shivraj refused to see Rangeelay.

After Shivraj's father's death, he returned to the ashram carrying a small tin trunk. The attitude of the ashram inmates seemed to have changed towards him; it was now like an orphanage to him. The offerings from home had stopped coming and Swamiji did not consider it necessary to cajole him any longer. The first time Shivraj had come to the ashram his father had sent two bags of wheat, one bag of jaggery and a pair of shirts with him. But now that source had suddenly dried up. At night, when Shivraj slept on the plinth under the open sky, tears would come to his eyes.

Being a village boy accustomed to living in the open air,

he soon got tired of the daily drudgery within the four walls of the ashram. In addition, every night he had to press Swamiji's legs which galled him no end.

One day he escaped from the ashram and knocked about in the bazaar for sometime. Then he decided to while away some more time at the bus stand before returning to the ashram. At the bus stand he happened to see Sarnam Singh sitting there leaning over a chessboard

'Namaste, Driver Saheb.' Sarnam Singh's familiar face put new heart in him.

Taken aback, Sarnam Singh surveyed the boy. He looked so different from what he had been three months ago. 'Your father is dead?' he asked.

Shivraj's face clouded and tears came to his eyes. Sarnam Singh put his arm round Shivraj's shoulder and led him towards the thatched hut. Just then two boys from the ashram came there in search of Shivraj. Their eyebrows went up as they saw him sitting in the midst of the transport crew.

'A nice place to be at!' the senior boy said as he looked with undisguised contempt at Sarnam Singh. Shivraj got up, flustered. Sarnam Singh scowled at the boys. 'What are you doing here?' asked the boy.

'I'm standing here, what else? Have you no eyes?' Shivraj's innate rustic boldness suddenly asserted itself through his timidity. He looked at the senior boy with a deadpan expression. Sarnam was pleased. The boy had guts.

'Come to the ashram,' the senior boys said. 'It's Swamiji's order. "Catch him wherever you find him and drag him here," that's what Swamiji said. We have been looking for you all over the place.'

'I refuse to go back to the ashram,' Shivraj said. Sarnam laughed. The senior boy was incensed. 'Let's go,' he said, pushing the other boy before him as if he were herding sheep. 'Let him make an ass of himself for all I care. We'll tell Swamiji that he refused to come.' They went away muttering under their breath.

That day Sarnam Singh took Shivraj on a trip with him.
When they returned the following day, he put the boy up at
his house. News soon spread in the town that Sarnam Singh
had kidnapped a boy from the ashram. They were not
surprised. It was very much like Sarnam Singh. What else
could one expect from a drunkard and a meat-eater? Alas,
the boy would be ruined for good.

'That fellow Rangeelay has been after him for a long
time,' a man said. 'Now he'll train him as a pickpocket and
ask him to join his gang.'

'I hear the boy is a vagabond.'

'No, he's a Brahmin's son.'

'All the worse for it.'

Shivraj never went back to the ashram. He stayed in the
outer room of Sarnam Singh's house, and gradually became
a regular fixture there. The pious men of the town raised
accusing fingers at Sarnam Singh. But he was unconcerned.
He retaliated by telling juicy stories about the corrupt lives
of the swamis. This created bad blood between the Swami
and the town roughs. The feud continued for a long time.

One day, when Shivraj woke up in the morning, he found
Sarnam lying with him in his cot. His hand was resting on
Shivraj's chest. It was nothing new for Sarnam and Shivraj
should have got accustomed to it by now. In the beginning,
when Shivraj protested, Sarnam said, 'You remind me of my
own youth. Sixteen years ago I was very much like
you—smart, agile and simple.' He sighed. 'Alas, those days
will never return.' He held Shivraj's hand in his own, looked
wistfully at his fingernails, pressed his knuckles, and moved
his hand over his soft downy arm. Then, as if the spell had
broken, he said, 'Run away!'

Once Sarnam clutched Shivraj in his arms and digging
his face into his hair sighed deeply. 'Shivraj, look at me,' he
said, lifting his chin. Shivraj, fluttering to disengage himself
from his clasp, stared at him like a helpless bird. Relaxing
his grip Sarnam said, 'Shiva, I'm sure you were related to
me in your previous birth. No? Once I caught mother like

this. She slapped me in the face and then overwhelmed with maternal affection, started crying.' Shivraj's heart which was filled with revulsion suddenly melted. Sarnam did everything to please Shivraj and bought him the nicest things currently in vogue.

What kind of love is this? Shivraj wondered. And why does it stink? Where did it begin and where will it end? Shouldn't he draw a line somewhere and keep Sarnam Singh from overstepping it so that their love was saved from festering?

Translated by Jai Ratan

Pages from a Diary

Bhupen Khakhar

When we left the Garden he was impatient to reach home. I was crossing the road slowly. Jitubhai had already crossed over, weaving his way between the rickshaws with not a worry for himself; then he waited on the other side impatiently. I was halfway to the other side and had just managed to avoid the last cyclist in my way, when he asked, 'Where is the scooter?'

I said, 'Next to the Acharya Book Depot. So we will have to go round the circle.'

'Come, walk a little faster.'

He was soon standing near the Acharya Book Depot. Then he said, 'Which scooter?'

'The grey one.'

'There are three here.'

'Here, this one.'

I had to obey the authority in his commanding voice. I ripped out the scooter key from the back pocket of my trousers and started the scooter.

'Which way?'

'The lane next to the fire-brigade station.'

Impatience, curiosity and eagerness to arrive were Jitubhai's. That's why he had been commanding me. I too was aware that this relationship was to last no more than half an hour. Both of us would forget each other within a day. There was no joy or excitement in my mind. There was a weariness, a monotony in the chain of happenings in such relationships.

I knew what kind of house it would be. A house with a rexine-covered sofa, a mini swing, ceiling fan, and walls painted white or grey . . . Lost in thought, I reached the third floor. He had already climbed the staircase ahead of me. I saw him press the bell of room number 305. I climbed the stairs and stood behind Jitubhai. He too was breathless. The door opened three inches.

Jitubhai: Key.

The door shut. Two minutes later a bunch of keys was held out by the fingers of a child. She wore bangles on her wrist. Jitubhai took the key.

He unlocked the house right opposite. Inside, an office table, under it a mattress gathered into a roll. Jitubhai switched on the fan. The glass window was shut. The typewriter on the table was covered. Since I wasn't certain where to sit, I pulled out the chair that was pushed into the space under the table and sat on it. The lower fringe of his shirt touched my mouth. Once in a while it flapped across my face when the wind blew.

Jitubhai: Wouldn't you like to stay here?

I shuddered at the thought of spending the night in that room with no ventilation. I lied. 'I have to catch the morning bus to Ahmedabad at six.'

'Go from here.'

'I have to collect some office papers from home. Besides, I haven't told my people at home, either.'

We both knew that this first encounter was also the last one. Jitubhai took off his cap and shirt and stood close to the chair. For the first time I looked at his face in the stark tubelight. An illness years ago had scarred it. The shining head, the sweat-drenched and pockmarked face looked ugly. Moreover, the thin lips made it look cruel too.

A hoarse voice emanated from the tall strong body.

'The building gate closes at nine every night, so be quick.'

With this he moved the typewriter with a jerk, and sat on the table. Before my eyes I now saw the white vest, the white dhoti and the phallus that sprang from it. I looked up. The pockmarked cheeks were smiling. Both eyes were shut to a slit, like the eyes of a Chinese.

He said, 'All well?'

I said, 'Let's skip this today.'

'Why?'

'Some other time.'

'You know as well as I do that—'

'What?'

'We shall never meet again.'

He caught my hand. Involvements, allurement, attraction had disappeared from my heart. I was thinking of paintings. A complete canvas full of white vest, the white dhoti and the slight transparency that revealed the phallus. I tried to get up from the chair. He took my hand, made me sit and said, 'What's wrong today?'

'I'm not in the mood.'

'What happened to your mood? Did I do something wrong?'

'No, just feeling off.'

'Come on, for my sake.'

I stayed there till nine for the sake of a man I would never meet again in my life.

Translated by G.N. Devy

O Pomponia Mine!

Sultan Padamsee

Shall I knot my tie a little more superbly,
O Pomponia mine?
A little more because we dine at the Astoria
To have bubbles in our wine?

You will wear your black, I think,
The new one, made of Agatha's heirloomed lace,
And add a touch of colour to your face
And leave a little on the glass from which you drink.

We shall play it bravely; only,
Pomponia, alone.
We shall never groan
Even if the rolls are hard,
And the prices on the card
Make us feel a little lonely.

Never mind,
I shall touch my tie,
And lie that we are of a different kind.

You will smile back,
A small cry of laughter in your eyes,
Underneath the hair that loves disguise
You will smile back.

They shall never know,
This is the toxin that adds flavour to our life,
Never know
That you are not my mistress nor my wife.

Epithalamium

Sultan Padamsee

LENIA: Is the night not sufficient darkness
To cover the slight defect of my limbs?
And you who have lain with me often,
Is custom not fertile enough for your embrace?
I have not taunted you in your moments,
Nor shrewed you in the hours before the sun
When my body was hot with expectation,
And yours as impotent as a sterile man.

Tell me Marius why then tonight when
I have watched the crowd surge
Into itself, so that I am in heat
For the embraces of a lover,
You are cold. Have I suddenly lost
The beauty I am noted for?
Have I ceased to be Lenia,
More than the harlot of high places?

MARIUS: It's not that, indeed it is not so.

LENIA: Do you find me suddenly coarse?
Am I not versed in the lore of the Hebrews?
Do I not worship the gods of Greece?
Do you find me coarse and unfaithful?
Could I not have had lovers,
Waiting for you?

Am I not a woman? And before you
Many have told me, men from Araby
And others, that the two scars on my thigh
Kindle them to a further desire,
So that they cannot resist my breasts
And must couple with me many times
Till they lie exhausted with the loss
Of their fluid: only I waited
With my wants not disposed of.

MARIUS: All this I know Lenia and I am weary—
Can you not understand that a man
Sometimes desires and sometimes not?

LENIA: Untrue, Marius, as untrue as your love—
Does it not even sateen your organ
To know that you alone in a single
Embrace completely involve me?

MARIUS: Listen Lenia, I shall explain—
Not for love of you for you are a harlot,
Even a witty harlot, but I must
Remove this heat of the sun
Of the City. Sometimes my thoughts
Take fire and as in verse
The lines turn forth. Listen then, Lenia,
My beloved of the moment, and
Take your fingers away from my pouch,
For in the moment of relief I feel cool,
And your hand is irritating,
Not enkindling, and listen—
Three walls there were
And a road along them—
A weary road along them.
The walls and the vales
Were lined with women.
Below the cross was a man of thirty,

A wasted face of much beauty,
He was made indifferently well—
But nothing to me,
A lover of women.

Three hills there were
And a crowd between them
People spitting and cheering.
The hills and the vales
Were lined with women.
On the cross they nailed
This thief and sinner,
And I felt pity.
They had taken away his garments
He was made indifferently well—
Yet nothing to me
But an object of pity
And strangely, a little love—
But nothing to me,
For I, Lenia, am a lover of women.
Three nails there were
Two were bright and one was rusty
They went into his left palm
And his two feet and his right palm.
A sweat was upon me
My skin pricked up
A lust as faint as the breeze
Of your stranger Samaria
Awoke me and left me.
Three nails there were
And the valleys below were mingled with
women.

I pitied this man,
Though my blood had beat faster,
For you know Lenia
That I am a lover of women, not men.
Thrice did he cry out,

And into my belly came
The gear of desire,
But I pitied the man;
Only that they had hurt him inflamed me,
And I was a god, cruel and loving,
They raised him and he cried out
In thirst—
For pain and fear are thirsty things.
I wined a sponge as a god who is loving
And I galled it as a god who is cruel,
And gave it to him.
But he was not thirsty enough.

I grew angered, and my love
And his pain and the dark sky
Grew together, and I knew
I must enter this man
In sensuous pain.
Three hours passed—
In the vales below the women
Waited and watched him
And desired him
Till I too grew mad with their fire.
And I seized a spear
And entered his body—in my haste
Below his right side—
This cooled me
For I am a lover of women, not men.
He died crying strange things.
The women jeered him and the men
Cried out strangely,
And as he died, my mind
Grew clouded,
And I gambled with the soldiers
For his garments and won.
I seized them and in that barren
Place which you Jews call Golgotha,

Behind a rock I buried my face
In the lice-ridden cloth.
In my madness I remembered
The beauty of women, their thighs
And waists and their hair,
Their breasts . . .

LENIA: Did you not think of me?

MARIUS: They were as nothing, as the
Dust, and I was no longer
A lover of women.
I went from that place
To the Jew whom we Romans call John,
And desired him and I have
Come here defiled.
For the body of John stroked my body
And the full lips of John
Stroked my body—
I am weary of delight.

LENIA: Look on me Marius, am I not desire?
My body is creamed and desireful.

MARIUS: The full lips of John
Stroked my body,
And the red nails of John
Did vile things and made
My body soft.

LENIA: Listen Marius, you are no poet.

MARIUS: I will not remember those things,
The white disease of the body of John.

The winds come down from
The mountains and Marius slept again
In the arms of a woman.

And So to Bed

Sultan Padamsee

A nd so to bed,
It always ends in bed.
The fires at London to light you to bed,
And the bombs of the Germans to chop off your head.
The end of the writers of lyrics,
The popular songsters, the songs of their mothers,
The lullabies that once rocked you to sleep.
The rocking and shaking of aerial warfare,
It all ends in bed.
To be born, to couple in the way of the ancients,
Or the way of the angels,
To die and be lain in the comforting earth,
Is to lie like the dead.
To lay back the covers, turn out the lights,
To sleep and be shaken and bred,
To make merry and slacken and wed
To live in excess and then lead,
Is the bearing, the wedding, the bedding, the dead,
It all ends in bed.
To dream in the conscious,
To wanton and flourish
Or sedulous ape the sages and martyrs,
To conceive the greatness, the godlike,
The heroes, the harlots, the poets,
Is to wait until dead,

Is to wait for the sanction of bed.
And late one night
There flew overhead,
A plane that had lost its way,
So it dropped its bombs,
And passed along
And passed along its way.
And the bombs of the plane
Blew the poet from bed
And the ugly man and the harlot
Who danced and died twice,
The Keeper of inns and
The bald-headed barman, they found
Them all in the neighbouring fields,
And they covered them up
Because they were dead.

The candles that shine in the morning for light,
And the angels that stand to keep in the night,
Were waiting and longing
In vain for the fires to light them to bed,
And the merciful choppers to chop off their heads,
They waited and watched and longed to be dead.

The Jungle

Madhav G. Gawankar

Deep, dense forest. Hairy and sweaty. I met Lily at Karnala. A very safe, protected place. Green and clean. I offered him cold coffee when he wanted something 'hot'. The sky was clear. Just like his innocent soul. He said, 'Many guys have deceived me. They cheated me. They pretended to be gay. Now, many of them are married. Please don't do that. Be my friend. Be my life partner. Treat me as your wife.' . . . He touched my heart. Lily, a flower boy so soft and smooth. Silky and milky. He caressed me. He wasn't looking careworn then. I didn't know that he had been beaten by his dad. He had been driven away. He was a bird without shelter. He had lost his job. His colleagues had tortured him as well. He never spoke. He never uttered a single word of sorrow. The storm lay in his heart. A deeply buried cyclone . . . He was like a sylph: merry and holy. I had never seen such beauty before. Slim, tender, fair . . . Hot like a volcano flower. We were free finches. He was very happy to know that I was a bachelor. He kissed me and whispered, 'I will never forget you. Though I go back to Bombay, I will be with you again.' I was not only his 'hubby,' but his 'babe' too.

Lily's green eyes were like stars. I didn't know then that they were only shooting stars. I still remember that rainy night. He wanted my sweaty, hungry body. I enjoyed his pointed nipples, his rosy lips, girlish moonface . . . specially the fragrance of his body . . . just like sandalwood. 'Give me a child,' he whispered. He had an impossible dream in his pious heart: to give birth to a baby, which would look just like me. 'God, give me that power,' he cried. Countless drops of joy took us to heaven, a place of bliss. It was not my first experience but what Lily gave me, other boys couldn't. When he patted me on my bare back, I felt as if my mother was with me. That wet night provided me a warm blanket of peace and true affection.

The days passed. I had to come back to Ratnagiri. Lily went to Bombay. I never received a letter; not even a small chit from him. He had not given me a phone number. I thought of him constantly. He came to me in my dreams. One day I decided to go to Bombay on official work. I had to do an 'on the spot' report for my newspaper. The Chief Editor said, 'Do come back within two days. I need to send you to Pune.'

'Yes sir,' I said like a truant schoolboy.

Bombay! Shining showcity. A veritable bhelpuri—tasty and risky. Before doing the 'on the spot report', I ran to Dharavi. I wanted to meet Lily, my fair boy. . .

A small girl opened the door.

'Does Hrishikesh stay here?' . . . I took his real name. She looked at me with surprise, as if I was asking about a ghost. She was Hrishi's cousin sister. She said, 'Don't you know . . . he committed . . . suicide.'

I couldn't believe it. 'When? When and why did he do that?' I almost screamed. An old woman who was probably Lily's mother, came out of the house. She understood my condition. She probably guessed who I was. She used to meet Lily's boyfriends. Lily's father was a rude monster, he spoiled that flower. Lily's mother told me the whole story. That old monster used to give him give him the worst traetment possible so that he would leave his 'habit'. But he never listened to his father. So his father drove him away. When he was sleeping on the footpath, he was brutally raped by a beggar. What a dirty, demeaning experience! He died of shame and fear; humiliation and disappointment.

They said he had killed himself three month ago. His

mother gave me the exact date. But he had met me at Karnala two months earlier.

I started perspiring. A glass of water did not help. Who did I meet? Whom did I sleep with? Only a soul? A bundle of wishes? A shadow of wet dreams? Where is my Lily now? I heard his lovely words coming from the dark, 'I will be with you again'.

I couldn't say anything to those poor souls. I had no wish to meet Lily's father. He . . . my Lily . . . had ended his life under 'double fast Virar'. He is still wandering . . . waiting for a sweet little baby with my round face. While playing with the curly hair on my chest, Hrishikesh had said, 'I love this jungle.'

Now I think, life itself is a mystic jungle, isn't it?

The Slaves

Hoshang Merchant

I met Mazhar one spring at the gay park. We looked at each other for an hour, then another and another. He was stout and strong, stronger than I at any rate. I'd expected him to make the first move. But I had to do it.

He thought me to be a foreigner and he didn't speak English. I did not disappoint him. I kept up my banter liberally peppered with accented Urdu.

I brought him home across the railway tracks separating Red Wills from the Public Garden. My room was bare like my heart. He took me standing up against the window. I felt suffocated as he entered me with a push. The window flew open and my curious neighbours had their curiosity satisfied.

Next day I heard a whimpering at my window. I looked out to see a madman, hirsute like me, with long hair, long beard. He could be love-mad. He could be god-mad. He moaned for about an hour at my window. I let him groan in ecstasy or pain. When I left for work I saw a mound of fresh deposit at my doorstep. I covered the stink with some fresh earth.

One night Mazhar brought a Christian girl to my home. He took her on the floor of my bare living room. I slept fitfully in the bedroom next to the living room listening to every moan. The girl dressed. A cross glistened on her impossibly lean frame. She probably needed food. Mazhar paid her fifty rupees. He felt like a man. She looked like a poor girl. I felt bad for her.

Mazhar would always take me from behind and then I would take him from behind. Like good friends we'd take turns. An older friend told me tales of machismo during the Nizam's rule: He and his friend could not decide on the male and female roles in bed. So they frigged each other standing up all night. Equality does not mean sameness, it merely means reciprocity.

Mazhar had no father. His mother ran a boarding house. First the maternal uncle, whose ward he was, used Mazhar. Then all the male boarders started using Mazhar. When he grew up he started using the servant girls. He felt like a master. They were his sex slaves.

Mazhar had big hands. He was an ironsmith, 'welder' they called him. His elder brother, now married, owned the smithy. An impossibly thin, mousy boy worked there. He loved Mazhar. Once he followed me up to my doorstep since he knew me to be Mazhar's friend and I guessed he had a relationship with Mazhar too.

Sure enough, Mazhar brought him home one day. By then I'd moved to a Muslim home in a largely Brahmin neighbourhood, and I occupied an attic where neighbours couldn't pry. Mazhar offered me the boy. I declined. Mazhar offered to let me watch. I accepted.

The boy undressed. Mazhar made the boy undress him. His fat body appeared from the clothes and his little penis showed from under his fat belly. The thin boy offered his lean ass standing up. Mazhar entered him from behind with force after wetting his dick with his own spit which he spat onto his hand and rubbed onto his dick. The boy let out a groan. But I could tell he did this on cue to increase his master's excitement.

Then Mazhar began his in-and-out strokes of the pelvis. The pelvic thrusts became fiercer and fiercer. The boy was perspiring. It was a warm August afternoon and our attic was sealed shut against any intrusion. The boy, also an ironsmith, withstood every blow.

He bent a little with each blow, groaning, perspiring, but straightened again only to bend and groan again under another thrust.

'Leave him! He'll die!' I cried.

'When will he die?' mocked Mazhar. His dick had slipped out at my sudden interruption. He quickly re-entered him.

He came inside the boy. Once. Twice. Thrice. Then when the boy begged mercy he let him go. I gave the boy ten rupees out of pity. The boy asked Mazhar too for an equal amount.

'Don't teach him bad habits,' Mazhar admonished me.

Whenever Mazhar would visit we'd ask each other: Whose turn?

'Mine, mine!' I'd unfairly clamour and mount him.

Once Mazhar wondered: 'It is I who fucks everyone; why is it that I let you fuck me?'

Mazhar was an illiterate. He worked all day with iron. He fucked prostitutes and servants. And he let me fuck him.

One rainy night Mazhar jumped the low wall of my walled-in ground floor apartment, for I had moved across the street from my poet's attic to a one-bedroom flat. He asked for vaseline himself and smeared it on my dick. Then he lay on his stomach and slowly made me enter him. He was on his knees and as I ever so gently slipped into him, Mazhar spread his legs wider and wider until there was no space left between my navel and his buttocks and his stomach and the mat. As I came inside him Mazhar too groaned and left a spot of wet semen on the mat.

Next morning I found a limp ten-rupee note on the wet grass. Mazhar never reappeared. I asked at the Friend's Medical Hall where he used to hang out and they told me he'd left for the Gulf. Perhaps he was striking iron or gold there; breaking stones, sifting sand.

I was followed in the streets by mad men, boys, prostitutes. Then one day I met a boy who knew Mazhar.

'He was afraid of me,' the boy said. 'I beat him up once.'

'But he fucked well,' I protested.

The boy looked at me with horror, knowing it would be his turn some day, as he had probably secretly hoped it would be.

When I moved house yet again I remembered I had left behind a ball of darkly violet opium I bought once from Mazhar on the kitchen shelf. My landlord must have discovered it and told my neighbours I was a slave to opium too.

*

I share Room 11A with Darius. Darius at the moment is curled on the bed adjacent to me in his underpants.

A knock. I get out of bed.

Before I pull on my pants a thin boy enters.

'Where's Darius? Don't tell me he's left and left all his things behind.'

I mumble something and turn in. The boy takes a once over at my pubic hair before leaving!

I snooze. An hour, maybe two.

Lights go on. It's a hot Delhi night. I poke my head out from under the light bedsheet which I've torn from the mattress to cover myself.

'Hello!'

'Hello Uncle! Don't sleep on the bare mattress. Bugs will get you.'

'Don't call me uncle! Though I'm forty and my hair is white, my heart is young. Call me Hoshang.'

The boy undresses with his back to me showing a superb torso. I see a long dick hanging between his legs from the back.

The bathroom door won't shut. He showers. Then leaves the shower tap running. Gently. He's in there for three minutes, then five more. Maybe ten more.

He unwraps his towel and pulls on his bermudas again

with his back to me. The shorts are printed with the
BATMAN logo.

'You're certainly at ease with your body! Did you learn
that at the gym?'

'No! At home!'

'You must have young parents.'

'In their fifties. Slightly older than you.'

'Well,' I say. 'I shock people when I say I sleep on the
same bed naked with my sister.'

We share a cigarette. He tells me he's going to the 'Uran
Academy' at Rae-Bareilly.

We share the same bed. He dozes off. I go to my own bed.

He can't sleep. He opens his eyes.

'It's hot.'

'Try the cold-shower therapy.'

'What's that?'

'In my day masturbation was taboo. Doctors
recommended cold showers.'

He smiled. He kept looking at me.

I saw the bulge in his pants dancing.

He was making it dance.

I was naked in bed. I wrapped a blanket over myself and
climbed into his bed.

I groped between his legs. He took my hand away from
his ass to his dick, turned up, erect, over his stomach.

I made him slip off his bermudas. My blanket half
slipped off by itself.

'Is it big?'

'Yes!'

He gave a shy look at my penis. 'Why isn't it getting big?'

'I'm old. Encourage it!'

'Move it up and down,' he said pointing to his penis. I
bent to put my lips to it. He pushed me away, an athlete.

I sat up in bed behind him. He feared for his ass. I touched
his nipples and then down the hairline over his pectorals to
his pubic hair. He got out of bed.

I tried to put my lips to his penis again. Thwarted again.

He went into the shower. I followed. I reached for the soap.

'That's no good.'

Under the water he began masturbating himself.

'Are you a virgin?'

'No.'

'When was your first time?'

'Forget it! I've just come! I do it five times a day!'

'I know it. Let me help you.'

He stands on tiptoe. He parts his legs. I thrust my left hand index finger up his ass while vigorously moving my right hand up and down his penis shaft.

Three gloriously white drops of semen splutter out as they do in gay comics. He wouldn't let me taste them. I rub my hand over his dick head. He convulses in pain then watches me lick his semen off my hands in disbelief.

Poems from a Vacation

S. Anand

Anand Speaks:

I want to be true to my name:
We were both alone
Then I met you
I will not let you commit suicide
I will tame you, fox, with the leash of love
                              Signed
                              L'il Prince.

Anand Writes from a Vacation as Home:

I'm no more the same
I'm a Brahmin ass:
Eat/sleep . . . eat/sleep

When letters arrive
six at a time
I fear my father
But I say nothing to his jibes

Writing this I remember Kundera:
The mother reads a fourteen-year-old's diary
And they are all laughing at her
In fear, I burst into a sweat

But writing this
I'm already better.

Night Queen

Mahesh Dattani

A tiny room with two doors. The side door leads directly to the street. The other door leads to the rest of the house. It is the sort of room which would be built for a paying guest who may need to come and go without disturbing the rest of the household.

We can see that the room is occupied by a single male. A bachelor's room with a huge poster of a muscle man on the cupboard. Some workout equipment can also be seen. A pair of jeans tossed on a chair. We also see a window.

However we can't see outside on the street because there is a night queen (raat ki raani) shrub acting as a mask.

It could do with some pruning. The shrub is shaking as a result of a strong wind.

We open on an empty stage. We hear an old woman calling out, 'Raghu! Ay, Raghu'. The strong wind blows some flowers into the room. Raghu enters the room through the side door and quickly shuts the windows.

Raghu is a young man in his mid-twenties. He wears trendy jeans that are a little too tight. His muscles are heavy and fairly well developed but they add a certain grace, rather than power, to his movements.

Raghu: (*calling out*) Come in!

(*Ash walks in. He looks around, still at the doorway. Ash is a little older than Raghu. He is good looking. A little self-conscious, which perhaps adds to his charm. Raghu picks up some of the flowers that had swept in.*)

Raghu: I like them on the branches.

Ash: Huh?

Raghu: The blooms. I don't like them on my floor.

Ash: Oh. (*preoccupied, looking around the room*) Why not?

Raghu: (*taken aback at the question*) Why not? I don't know. I just like them better when they are still up there. Besides, they lose their fragrance once they fall off. No point in sticking them in vases.

Ash: Pretty strong smelling.

Raghu: Do you need to go to the bathroom now?

Ash: Er—ya.

Raghu: (*pointing to the other door*) You have to go through that door. It's the first door across the living room. You might bump into my folks but don't mind. They are quite used to it.

Ash: Never mind. I'll go later.

Raghu: Sit down.

(*Ash continues to stand. Raghu is unsure now.*)

Ash: Why don't you shut the door?

(*Raghu looks at him for a while. He goes to the window instead and opens it. The wind blows in more flowers and dried leaves, before subsiding. Raghu stares at him.*)

Ash: What's your name?

Raghu: Babu.

Old woman's voice: (*off*) Raghu! Raghu?

Ash: Who is Raghu?

Raghu: (*throwing up his hands*) Alright. I am Raghu. I am so used to giving a false name. But you seem to be okay.

Ash: You didn't think so a while ago.

Raghu: Just out of habit I guess. (*Fishing out his card*) Here's my card. I work for Microland. Assistant Sales Manager. Here, take it.

(*Ash accepts the card and puts it in his wallet without looking at it.*)

Raghu: I might as well have yours.

Ash: Huh?

Raghu: Your card. Can I have your card?

Ash: (*putting his wallet back in his hip pocket*) No. I have run out of cards.

Raghu: Then I think I should have my card back.

Ash: Why are you nervous?

Raghu: What's your name?

Ash: Relax.

Raghu: What is your name?

Ash: I told you. Ash.

Raghu: Ash. I have used that one before!

Ash: That is my name.

Raghu: Is it short for Ashok or Ashish or Ashley?

Ash: Ash will do for you. Now that you know my name, you can shut the door.

(*Raghu moves slowly to the door and shuts it.*)

Ash: Leave the window open.

Raghu: Someone may peep in.

Ash: (*moving to the window*) For now. I will shut it after a while.

(*Pause*)

Ash: My grandmother wouldn't allow us to grow night queen. She said it attracted snakes. We grew up in a village named—a village.

Raghu: There's no danger of that here. Snakes, I mean.

Ash: I planted one anyway. Such strong fragrance!

Raghu: And did it attract snakes?

Ash: In my dreams.

(*Pause*)

Ash: I would go to sleep with the blooms on my body. And I would dream. The snake would slither into my bed, curl up over my belly, attracted by the scent. And I would imagine that it was attracted to my body. The warmth of my body. And I was aroused by the presence of the snake. The snake then turned into a man. A man who made love to me.

Old woman's voice: (*off*) Gayatri! Gayatri, are you asleep?

Ash: (*startled*) Who is that?

Raghu: My mother. She is senile. And an insomniac. Just

ignore her.

Ash: Who is Gayatri?

Raghu: My sister.

Old woman's voice: (*off*) Gayatri!

Raghu: (*going to the door*) Excuse me.

(*Ash surreptitiously takes out his wallet again and looks at Raghu's card.*)

Raghu: (*yelling through doorway*) Gayatri, see what she wants. I have a visitor!

(*Raghu comes back in. Ash quickly puts the card and wallet back in his pocket.*)

Raghu: Wow! I have heard some wild gay fantasies, but this one is something special. Snakes turning into sexy men. Though it should be obvious. I mean the snake being such a classic phallic symbol.

(*Ash looks at him displeased.*)

Raghu: Anyway, I am happy that you mentioned it. Only a gay man could have such a fantasy. So I am sure of you now.

Ash: What do you mean?

Raghu: For a minute I thought that you may be, you know, one of those.

Ash: One of those?

Raghu: Straight guys pretending to be gay so they can pick up someone, bash them up and take all their money.

Ash: Has it happened to you?

Raghu: Sure. Twice. Hasn't it happened to you?

(*Ash shakes his head.*)

Raghu: I can't believe it. You are probably the only one. Maybe you just know how to stay away from the wrong ones. Some people can tell a hetero guy a mile away. I think it's the way they walk.

Ash: Oh. And what about you? Can't you tell?

Raghu: Sometimes. But I am never too sure.

Ash: What do you feel about me?

Raghu: When you sat beside me on the park bench, I was pretty sure. But after a while I wasn't too sure.

Ash: Why?

Raghu: You didn't put your hand on my crotch.

Ash: And yet you invited me to your home.

Raghu: Well. I put my hand on your crotch. That's when I was sure. At least then I was.

Ash: And now you feel that I may be one of those.

Raghu: It doesn't matter even if you are. I am trained for combat. I bash up gay bashers.

Ash: You feel that would be necessary with me?

Raghu: You never know.

Ash: Do I look like a gay basher to you?

Raghu: Not now. Not after you told me your fantasy.

Ash: That was a lie.

Raghu: You mean it was a fantasy. There's a difference between a lie and a fantasy. What you just said was your fantasy.

Ash: The fantasy was a lie. I don't fantasize about snakes turning into men and giving me a blow job.

Raghu: So you made it up.

Ash: Yes.

Raghu: But that's what a fantasy is! It's not real, it's made up! So it can't be a lie if you made it up!

Ash: I lied about making it up! I don't fantasize. I don't fantasize!

Raghu: No. You don't understand. If you could invent such a story, then it is a part of your fantasy. Whether you really dreamed about it then, or it came to you now is immaterial. It is a part of you.

Ash: No! It can't be. I—I didn't invent the story. It was told to me. By someone in the park. And I passed it off as my own now.

Raghu: Why? What was the necessity? To impress me? I am impressed already. (*Suggestive*) Shall we close the windows now? The smell of the night queen is overpowering somehow.

(*Raghu doesn't wait for an answer. He moves to the windows and shuts them, gently slipping the bolt in.*

Raghu goes to Ash and slowly begins to caress his cheek. Ash stands frozen for a while. Raghu's hand moves slowly to Ash's breast.

Ash suddenly grabs Raghu's neck and starts to push him up against a wall.)

Ash: You know what I did to the guy who told me that story? I bashed him up. I beat him till he was pulp. I could have slit his throat and thrown him in the gutter! That's what he deserved. That's what you deserve!

Raghu: Get your hands off me, you swine!

Ash: Why? What will you do? Shout for help? Call the police? What can you do? Call your parents? Call your neighbours to help you? You don't deserve to be helped. You should be locked up in an institution.

Raghu: Who are you to decide that? Fuck you!

Ash: I know you would like to do that. I won't let you do that!

(Ash begins to punch him. Raghu lets out a cry of pain as he doubles up.)

Old woman's voice: (*off*) Raghu! Ae Raghu!

Ash: Go on! Tell her! Tell her: 'Mother! The man I picked up in the park to have sex with is beating me up!'

Old woman's voice: (*off*) Raghu! Who is that with you?

Ash: Tell her who I am.

Old woman's voice: (*off*) Raghu! Answer me!

Ash: (*beating him up*) Answer her! Tell her who I am.

Raghu: (*suddenly grabbing his wrist*) Ashwin Kothari.

(Ash is stunned for a moment at this disclosure. He backs away slowly.)

Old woman's voice: (*off*) Who is that in the house? Raghu!

Raghu: (*goes to door, yelling out*) Nobody! Just my friend! Go to sleep!

(Raghu looks at Ash. He moves slowly to him Ash suddenly makes a dash for the door. He tries to unlock it, but Raghu manages to grab him by the waist and drag him back into the room. Raghu beats him up. Ash resists but doesn't fight back.)

Raghu: Shall I tell her? Shall I tell her who you are?

Ash: Let me go! (*struggling*) Let go of me!

Raghu: You don't deserve to be anywhere near this house! (*Pause*)

Ash: (*gasping for breath*) Don't tell them. Just don't tell them!

Raghu: Let them know!

Ash: (*wheezing loudly*) I can't breathe! My asthma . . . I—I can't breathe! Please!

(*Ash is on the floor now trying hard to breathe. Raghu goes to the window and opens it. A strong wind blows in more dry leaves and flowers. Ash staggers to the window and lets out loud gasps as if he is fighting asphyxiation.*)

Old woman's voice: (*off*) Gayatri! Gayatri! See what that Raghu is doing!

Ash: (*weak*) Just let me go back to my room. Let's just pretend it all never happened. I won't say anything about you, if you . . .

Raghu: I can't just let you go now. And tomorrow . . .

Ash: Forget it. Forget we ever met. I won't bring it up again.

Raghu: And Gayatri?

Ash: What about her?

(*Pause*)

Ash: Surely you wouldn't tell her, would you? Then you will have to tell her about yourself.

Raghu: She knows. She knows about me. And I am going to tell her about you.

Ash: You mustn't! If you do, I will reject the proposal! I will say she is unsuitable.

Raghu: And then? Marry someone else?

Ash: That is none of your concern. Let me go.

Raghu: Get out!

(*Ash walks slowly to the door.*)

Old woman's voice: (*off*) Gayatri! Is there enough milk for the kheer? Is he coming alone?

(*Ash turns around and looks at Raghu.*)

Old woman's voice: (*off*) Gayatri!

Raghu: Wait! I am not going to let you get away without doing something first.

Ash: What do you want now?

(*Pause*)

Raghu: If you hadn't found out who I am . . .

Ash: I—I just want to stop people from doing it.

Raghu: Bullshit. If you hadn't—

Ash: I wouldn't have done anything. I am not gay.

Raghu: Bullshit. You would have sucked my cock tonight and come back tomorrow in the morning to meet my sister.

Ash: Look. If you wish I will come tomorrow and we could go ahead as planned. I could meet my parents and — and fix the date. I promise not to tell them about you, if you promise—

(*Ash stops himself, realizing what he just said.*)

Raghu: I promise not to tell your parents, if . . .

Ash: Don't bring my parents into this!

Raghu: I promise not to tell your parents, if . . .

Ash: (*hysterical*) What do you want from me? (*Pause*)

Raghu: I don't want anything from you, you scum.

Ash: Good bye.

Raghu: I want to give you something.

Ash: I don't want anything from you.

Raghu: You are going to get a nice present.

Ash: I don't want it.

Raghu: A present you will value for the rest of your life.

Ash: Alright! Give it to me and let me go out of this hell.

Raghu: Come back in.

Ash: What is it? What's the present?

Old Woman Voice: (*Off*) Gayatri! What time is he coming?

Ash: Can't you give it to me tomorrow?

Raghu: No. This is the only chance you will have.

Ash: What do I have to do?

Old Woman Voice: (*Off*) Raghu! Ae Raghu!

Raghu: (*goes to door and yells out*) I am busy with

preparations for tomorrow! Don't disturb me! Gayatri, see what she wants!

(*Raghu shuts the door and walks slowly towards Ash. A strong wind blows in some flowers again.*)

Raghu: Come and stand by the window.

Ash: No I won't.

Raghu: Ashwin. Ashwin Kothari.

(*Raghu turns off the light. The room is now lit only by the bed lamp and the night queen is seen in silhouette caused by the street light. It looks almost surreal. Ash walks slowly to the window. The wind continues to blow through the night queen.*)

Raghu: Smell that?

Ash: How can I not?

Raghu: (*gently*) Yes. It is perfect. The perfect night.

Ash: It is very quiet all of a sudden.

Raghu: So it is.

(*Pause*)

Raghu: It is time to go to sleep.

Ash: Huh?

Raghu: It is time. You said so yourself.

Ash: Did I?

Raghu: At your grandmother's you said.

Ash: Oh that. That wasn't me. I told you it was someone else.

Raghu: It is your fantasy. I know about your grandmother, and your village. Gayatri tells me everything.

Ash: And . . . do you tell her everything?

Raghu: No.

(*Pause*)

Raghu: (*adding*) Only what she ought to know. And if I feel it necessary. And if circumstances force me to it. Which I am sure they won't. Will they?

Ash: (*sighing*) Do what you want.

Raghu: Good. That's settled. Now what was it you said? Or was it your grandmother? About snakes.

Ash: She said . . . she said, we mustn't grow night queen near our house. Its fragrance attracts snakes.

Raghu: And you believed her?

Ash: Yes.

Raghu: And yet you planted one.

Ash: No. I didn't. I imagined I did.

Raghu: Oh that's even better! Well. You are lucky. This one is real.

Ash: (*touching the plant through the window*) Yes. There's no doubt about it.

Raghu: So what do you do now?

Ash: I—I don't understand.

Raghu: What you do every night. Not now, but . . . How old were you then?

Ash: You mean . . . the first dream?

Raghu: Yes. The first time.

Ash: Oh. Maybe thirteen, fourteen. No! I was fourteen!

Raghu: How are you so sure?

Ash: Because that is the day I saw . . . No! I won't tell you.

Raghu: So you are fourteen. And this is the day you've seen something you won't tell me.

Ash: Yes. It is night now.

Raghu: Good. Go on.

Ash: It is time to go to sleep.

Raghu: Be my guest. Go on.

(*Ash looks at him. He walks to the bed and lies down on it. The light from the bed lamp puts the focus on his face. Raghu begins to pluck some of the blooms. The wind blows again. Raghu goes to Ash.*)

Raghu: (*placing the flowers on Ash's abdomen, one by one*) The fragrance is intoxicating. It puts you to sleep.

Ash: Hmm.

Raghu: And . . .

Ash: (*closing his eyes*) I don't know now.

Raghu: And you dream.

Ash: Yes. That I do.

Raghu: Tell me your dream.

Ash: I—I can't.

Raghu: You talked about it earlier.

Ash: That was different.

Raghu: Why?

Ash: You didn't know me then.

Raghu: I don't know you. I don't know who you are. So tell me.

Ash: (*with some difficulty*) I dream that I am sleeping under the shrub. The night is warm, although it has rained. The shrub is of course in full bloom. I look up and I can see the bunches of tiny white flowers. Hundreds of them. And I see the snake. Amidst the flowers. Drinking in the fragrance, like I do. I smile at the snake. He comes down and moves up my legs. He curls up on my abdomen. I am aroused. Like I was aroused that morning when I saw my brother lying on his bed, stroking himself. I watched . . . I watch. The snake turns into a human being. A man. A beautiful man. My brother. My brother makes love to me. And I cry. I am filled with pleasure that I cannot contain . . . I burst with joy. A fountain erupts. Tears and semen flow. My brother vanishes. The snake moves away. The shrub grows. The flowers fade away leaving nothing.

(*Ash opens his eyes and looks up at Raghu. Raghu moves closer to Ash.*)

Raghu: So. You see who you are. Don't you?

Ash: (*turning away from him*) That is not all!

Raghu: There are more dreams?

Ash: Nightmares! Living ones. Real, not fantasy! Don't you want to hear them too?

Raghu: No. All I wanted you to do was admit you are gay. You may go now.

Ash: Don't! You hate me, don't you? Go on, say it!

Raghu: I pity you.

Ash: Who are you to feel superior? You think you have it easy? Just because you have this—(*gesturing to the room and bed*) this arrangement, this setup. Just because you are smart enough and strong enough to defend yourself, you have a sister who understands you, you have a secure job and all that, it doesn't make you an . . . (*stopping*) Yes. It does make you superior somehow. You can tell the world to fuck off.

Raghu: (*sincerely*) I am sorry.

Ash: He beat me up.

(*Pause*)

Raghu: You don't have to talk about it, I understand.

Ash: My brother beat me up. I slept with him the next day. I wanted it. For real. I should have been happy just dreaming about it . . . He hit me hard. The next evening, he took me out. To the park. He showed me those guys, looking around, waiting for a sexual partner. A stranger. He told me how unhappy and miserable they were. They looked unhappy and miserable to me. And ugly. And I didn't want to be a part of that. I didn't want to be so ugly and repulsive! In my brother's eyes they were worse than lepers. And I was my brother's favourite. In his eyes, I didn't want to be so ugly. Walking alone at night in a park eyeing strange men. Waiting at corners for someone to stop and stare. Following a man into the bushes. Unloading my burden as quickly as possible. Pulling up my pants and walking away before I could feel the shame. Going home as if nothing had happened. Till the next evening. (*Tearful*) I saw! You asked me to see myself? I saw myself in my brother's eyes and I wanted to die. I promised my brother I would change. I told him to help me. I wanted him to help me get out of the hell. (*Looking at him*) I hate myself.

Raghu: You shouldn't have asked your brother for help.

Ash: I should have asked you. Where were you when I needed you?

Raghu: I was right there. But you didn't look for me. You looked for your brother.

Ash: It is too late now.

Raghu: Bullshit.

Ash: I will marry Gayatri.

Raghu: Why?

Ash: I don't want to be ugly any more.

(*Raghu goes up to him and slaps him.*)

Raghu: Look at me.

Ash: I don't want to! You are ugly too.

Raghu: (*shouting*) Look at me! I am your brother. I am the one you dreamed of. And you look ugly in my eyes! Oh yes! You are ugly. And you will be uglier. Pretending to love her—

Ash: I do.

Raghu: (*ignoring him*) Pretending that she turns you on. That you are in love with her. That everything will be alright after marriage. Such pretence! And when you sleep with her, you will be groaning extra loud with pleasure, shutting your eyes, thinking of your snake god or whatever, and penetrating her with those images in your mind. Pretending, pretending all the fucking way!

That's really shitty ugly! And in case you can't make those wonderful fountains erupt, she will look at you, questioning you. And you will be ugly enough to lead her to believe that she isn't good enough. That she doesn't satisfy you. You will watch her being filled with self-doubt. And you will give your ugly sympathy to her. You will say to her it's alright, you still love her. And she will be grateful to you! That's ugly! See that! See all that and tell me if that isn't ugly.

Ash: No! That won't happen! I know it won't!

Raghu: (*drowning him*) That is not ugly, that is simply repulsive. Hideous! To think it won't happen. You stink!

Ash: (*running to the door*) I don't believe you! I refuse to believe you!

Raghu: (*stopping him from opening the door*) Why didn't you say that to your brother? You should have refused to believe him!

Ash: How could I? He is my brother!

Raghu: You don't exist for your brother! You are ugly to him! He doesn't want an ugly brother.

Ash: (*gasping loudly*) No! Noooo!

Raghu: (*not letting him off*) But he is ugly too. Why don't you think of him as ugly? In your eyes he should be ugly.

Ash: (*hoarse with crying*) But I love him! I love him!

Raghu: (*shaking him*) But you never asked him to change. Why didn't you beat him when you saw him masturbating? Why didn't you beat him up when you saw him with his girlfriend? Why didn't you tell him that unless he slept with a man, he is as ugly as a leper? Why didn't he go down on his knees and plead with you to help him? Why?

Ash: I need some air! Why isn't there any air in this room? (*Ash goes to the window and starts to pull at the shrub.*)

Ash: Get rid of this plant! The smell is stifling me!

(*Ash starts tearing down the shrub. Raghu watches him.*)

Ash: Get rid of this! I will be able to breathe again! Help me! Why won't anyone help me! (*Ash grows weaker as he pulls at more flowers and branches. Finally he is just hitting at the plant blindly. He gives up after a while, totally exhausted. Ash falls to his knees, spent.*)

Ash: God! Why won't you help me? God!

Raghu: God won't.

(*Ash looks up at him. Pause*)

Ash: (*rising*) But you will.

Raghu: I don't know. I am just as scared as you are. I too am looking for help—from you. Help me.

(*They move towards one another. They embrace. Holding on to each other tightly.*)

Ash: Help me, Raghu.

Raghu: Help me, Ashwin.

(*They begin to kiss.*)

Old woman's voice: (*off*) Raghu! Ae Raghu! What are you doing?

(*Raghu begins to laugh. His laughter grows. Ash joins him in the laughter.*)

Old woman's voice: (*off*) Raghu!

Raghu: (*shouting*): I am playing Mother! At last I am playing!

(*They move clumsily to the bed, still laughing. They grow silent for a while, looking at each other.*)

Raghu: We should give each other the chance to

bloom—at least at night.

(*They sit cross-legged on the bed, facing one another, just looking at each other, too excited now to do anything. Slow fade-out. Fade-out last on the night queen.*)

Gandu Bagicha

Namdeo Dhasal

I
No flower
No leaf
No tree
No bird
Only kama's play
Musk scent
The sound of dry leaves underfoot
O my love, O the beauty of gardens!

What shall I say
Your full-throated weeping
Morning and night
Silence
And homeguard parades
A romeo
A Councillor
Yellamma's dancing skirts
An all India Women's Conference.

Street whores
and gold
Political crows sitting on a branch
The drug addict
Pickpocket, thief

The destroyed jungle of a pained heart
Gandu Bagicha Gay Gardens
What sorrow shall you sing
Boys have become that way now
Praise and blame
Consciousness and torpor
The darkness of doom
The golden shore

The deafening roar of chaos
and the death of doom
The stigma of a secret love
Its life
The dead of separation
The sympathetic grave
Loveliness and magic fear
Behind every word lurks a shamed face
Shall I take you nakedly on a bed?

Gandu Bagicha
The unsatiated lust of Yakṣhas
I wear your crown
of radiant African pain
My hurt heart is closed
Words don't open its doors
Banners and complaints
A bad poet like me
speaks in vernaculars
There's no recognition
no revelation

Pain peers out of a black burkha
Your life underfoot
Eternity's stork flutters its wings under a tree
Let me take in the womb-darkness of mud

My dreams are shattered
Let me stay naked
Wipe me with the sky and cast it away like a rag

The shroud of leaves lies in your front yard
The alphabet lost to you
lies among the cemetery's pigs
Isn't it nice to become a eunuch
(your hair in womanly tresses)
To be fucked at midnight by a stud?
Sister one day he too will die, paralysed
It's only us who are infatuated with our own beauty

The horsemen of the apocalypse flee
Graveyards sprout flowers
Ibsen's doll is a married Hindu lady
The terror of the labyrinth
Let us spill our seed on each other
Then I'll kiss your closed lips
Your sallow body I colour with my wings
You do not wish to open your sorrow's door
sitting silent under a tree
Should I wear shoes on lame legs?
Should I bell the cat?
Should I slay reality:
Light a lamp between a beginning and an end?

II
I've forgotten the garden

O friend! fry my torn heart and serve it on onions

Laxman fills my pocket
The Nawab of kababs feeds me
Time sweeps away the dust

in two worlds
Loneliness has been touched
Time's worm
Time's blind cockroach eats mud senselessly
autumn touches with its leaves
Illusion's condom burst
What then are you wearing
on this thing in your trousers?

I've forgotten the garden
O friend! fry my torn heart
and serve it on onions.

III
Not a soul on the street
Where are you hurrying?

You've been touched
by a first touch

Donkeys wag tails
Birds raise an alarm
The flowers have answered you on Death
On victory's star sleeps many a ghost
At the brothel you lost Galileo's pendulum
The widow gladdens her heart
The cripples play kabaddi
The lame sleep under rags
The leper cracks what's left of his knuckles
Homosexuals screw each other
to the strains of the nation's anthem

The street is soulless
you alone hurry along it.

Translated by Hoshang Merchant and the poet

Moonlight Tandoori

R. Raj Rao

1

During the last three months of my stay in England, I left the University of Warwick and moved into a room above the Moonlight Tandoori restaurant in the city of Coventry. University rules permitted a student to stay on campus for only the first year of his academic programme, and since I was on a one-year fellowship that commenced in January, I had to leave at the beginning of Michaelmas to make room for freshers. The months of October, November and December, when England's weather got increasingly fouler, I had to fend for myself; and accommodation being a tough and expensive affair, especially for foreign students from Third World countries, it was with the help of an Indian professor teaching at Warwick (I dare not mention his name) that I landed up at the Moonlight Tandoori, bag and baggage.

Moonlight Tandoori. Funny name for a restaurant, but then most Asian restaurants in Britain have names like that, catering to romantic notions about the subcontinent. But the name wasn't the only strange thing about the restaurant; there were other things too. Take the layout. There was no direct approach to my room from anywhere; to get to it, I had to wade through the over-full kitchen, making my way amid pots and pans and food in different stages of preparation. In the mornings when I left for the university, these and occasionally a couple of gambolling mice were my only hosts bidding me goodbye. But in the evenings when the restaurant opened, there were the cooks and waiters as well, who greeted me in a mixture of Hindi and English.

I soon discovered that my room on the first floor was surrounded by several other abandoned rooms, all in a state of disuse, full of junk. There was one, however, almost adjacent to mine, that housed an ornate dressing-table, and it was in this room that I made friends with him, as he sat in front of the gilded mirror, smoking, admiring his lovely hair.

His first act, as I peeped through the slightly ajar door, was to put out his cigarette and stand up in deference to me, a teacher almost twice his age. But once I assured him that I did not mind if he smoked, that I'd be happy if he treated me as an equal, his confidence was restored, and he offered me a cigarette and told me a little about himself: how, although only seventeen, he had come from Sylhet in Bangladesh to make money and send to his parents; how he hated life in England and hoped to return to Sylhet soon; how he picked up all the Hindi he knew from the Bombay movies that he saw on video, and English from his chums at school.

Though he told me his name on the very day we became friends, it took me a while to remember it. At first I simply referred to him as the little chap, for his smooth face and swollen cheeks indeed made him a bonny baby. Then I started calling him by his name, Khalid. Initially, I was even put off by his friendliness. Rather, I was suspicious. He came to my room a few days after we'd met and asked for my transistor radio, which I grudgingly gave. He said he wanted to listen to it in the kitchen while cooking. I was sure he was going to ask me for money, and I rarely lend money to fellahs.

What was more, he often barged into my room without knocking, kicking the door open like the angry young men of Hindi films. This, of course, could be viewed in two ways: it was an assault on my privacy if I was caught in an unguarded moment I'd rather have kept to myself; on the other hand, at times I deliberately took off my pants and masturbated, hoping he would walk in. But these calculations misfired, for he invariably came in at the wrong time.

Conversation, when we were safely locked up in my room, often revolved around sex. He would tell me about his encounters with prostitutes and the girls in his school, and a twinge of jealousy would tear through my chest. 'You look like Mithun Chakravarti,' I would say, ingratiatingly, and he would go red in the face. Then, confiding in me, he'd tell me how Ahmed, his uncle and employer, owner of Moonlight Tandoori, exploited him, and I would feel helplessly sorry, and my feelings would show.

Once when he entered, I was reading a book with a picture of a cow on the cover, and he found this so funny that he held his stomach and laughed. The laughter was contagious. After a while I found myself laughing too, unable to answer his questions on what the book was about (it was actually a lesbian novel), or why I was reading it, and we laughed till our eyes streamed and our bellies ached.

Soon it was clear Khalid merely sought an excuse to come up to my room every evening, whenever he was free from orders. Sometimes it was to play a game of numbers which we enjoyed greatly: you thought up a number in your mind, halved or doubled it, added or subtracted as you were instructed, and in a few minutes you were told what your number was. Or it was to ask me whether I wanted to have a haircut, say, and had to be shown the saloons.

By the end of October, I was writing the following entries in my diary: I love K: dangerous emotions developing. He's a little chicken. Feel fucked up. I'll be leaving in a couple of months. Because of him want to dress and look good . . . today he called me his darling, said he hasn't a friend in this country to whom he's so close.

2

I started having my dinner in the kitchen of Moonlight

Tandoori because it gave me a chance to feast my eyes on Khalid, his fragile body and husky skin, as he prepared naans in a large tandoori oven. There were, at any time, at least three or four hangers-on in the kitchen, distant relatives of Khalid and Ahmed, who belonged to rival Asian restaurants in the city. Notwithstanding their presence, Khalid would look at me slyly and smile. 'Why is your blood so cold?' he asked me one evening in his British Asian accent, as I was munching my food and he was putting hot naans on my plate, and wondered whether it was because I was a Hindu, whom he associated with cows and vegetarian food. The reason was that I was constantly complaining about the weather. That was a particularly rewarding day. Early in the evening he was bold enough to tickle me in the ribs in Ahmed's presence, much to my embarrassment. Later, as I sipped coffee in my room after dinner, he wanted to know why I was never seen in sleeping clothes. Before I could frame a convenient answer, he pouted his lips and went, as Ahmed called out to him from downstairs. Such acts made my heart pound, and fed my fantasies when I put out the lights.

Then came Guy Fawkes day. As soon as it grew dark, there were bonfires all around. Khalid came to the restaurant in a temper because Ahmed had cancelled his holiday at the last minute. He was hoping to walk through the town with his friends; he'd even bought firecrackers to celebrate. I was secretly happy—days when Khalid was away from the restaurant were unbearable. Yet I was pained, for I couldn't see him sulking. I tried to cheer him up by giving him a present, a Warwick University T-shirt. I said I hoped it would inspire him to study well and join the university. He accepted it shyly, and said, 'You should have bought a jumper for yourself, brother.' Then he showed me another T-shirt with the words 'Beep You Bastard' printed on it, which amused him very much. He tried out my present and looked a killer.

'You've bowled me over,' I told him, and he did not know

how to respond. 'Bhaisaab, it's okay if one of us was a woman,' he said with some hesitation. I pinched his cheeks. He shrieked and implored me to handle him gently, as a man would a woman. I told him we should be pen-friends. This didn't seem to interest him very much, and he changed the subject, asking me how I liked the fitting of his trousers. I inspected them and couldn't take my eyes off his cock. Then he reverted to the topic of pen-friends, and said I shouldn't look for grammatical errors in his letters. I took a sip of the alcohol-free beer he was drinking (halal beer in his lingo) and asked him if he minded. He said I could take anything I wanted. He wouldn't mind.

Before leaving my room that night, with his usual 'take care of yourself', Khalid sang two Bengali songs in a croaky, unmelodious voice. I suddenly saw him as terminally ill: he would go away, no matter what I did. But while I was around I was going to make the most of it.

3

I decided to have a heart-to-heart talk with Khalid. It was with some courage that I brought myself to tell him I wanted to speak to him. He was puzzled. Didn't we do that everyday? But this was different; it had to be private, within the confines of my room, preferably before the restaurant opened so that no one was around. 'What about?' he asked, his face growing serious.

The next day he did not pop into my room to say 'hi' when he came up to change into his working clothes. When I went down to see him, I found Ahmed scolding him for various lapses. After Ahmed left the kitchen, I asked him how he was. He was grumpy.

I brought up the topic again. When . . .? He evaded the question and continued to fret for a while. Then he promised to see me the next afternoon. But he was still uncertain what it was about. 'Give us a clue,' he said several times during the evening, chopping vegetables, kneading dough. It was my turn to be evasive.

As expected, he did not turn up at the appointed time. He arrived three hours later, at restaurant time, wearing my Warwick University T-shirt. 'Sorry brother,' he said as he rushed into my room, and left at once.

The whole of the next week, we weren't on speaking terms. I was even glad. But he wouldn't leave me alone. On the eighth day, he entered my room as if nothing had happened. I decided to cold-shoulder him. 'I'm busy,' I said, 'got to finish a paper,' and he went away. When I went down for dinner, he tried again, but I maintained the same strategy. Don't know how to cope, I wrote in my diary that night. K's playing havoc.

Eventually it was I who capitulated. As I was going to my room one evening, I found him in his, smoking. I knocked, and we became friends again. He said many sugary things that gladdened me. I took his hand, repulsed a little by the corns on his fingers, and kissed it again and again. Both of us were happy. But when he produced a ring from his pocket and said it was from his girlfriend, I felt awful. He's ragging me, he enjoys doing it, I told myself.

For a while I resolved not to confess to Khalid. Things improved. We even had sex mentally. Sometimes he would change his trousers in my presence. At other times he would discuss his wet dreams. Once he drew my attention to the hair on his legs and said everyone in his family had hairy legs. 'I'm going to make love to you,' I ventured to say, and put my head on his lap. He did not resist but spoke of my need to have a girlfriend. 'You are better than any girlfriend,' I replied. My day was made.

Then I was worried about his future. Was he going to slog it out in rotting kitchens all his life? I wished I could take him with me to India, to Bombay, to give him a decent education and change the course of his life. I sort of got to understand the cast of his mind and knew exactly how to humour him. When he sulked, I discovered it was not because of me, but because of problems with his parents or

Ahmed, often on account of his lafdas with the young Asian girls of the neighbourhood. 'You don't have the brains to tell who loves you,' I said to him once, when he was in a lousy mood, and brought him round. Ahmed unexpectedly walked into my room, and I had to cover up, saying, 'He's confessing.' Ahmed responded with an 'I haven't heard', shrugged his shoulders, and left the room.

4

Sometime around the middle of November, Khalid and I went out to the movies. It was on one of his off days. He picked me up at five in the evening, when it was already dark, and we walked to the city centre in the stinging cold. With a fur coat almost reaching my ankles, and a balaclava and gloves, I looked like a bandit and terrified people on the road. The film was *Ghost*. I bought Khalid a pack of Benson & Hedges cigarettes and paid for the tickets, although he protested, saying I was a guest in the country. On the way to the theatre, and later as the movie was on, I tried very hard to hold his hand, but he just wouldn't yield. Perhaps he would have, if we were in India or Bangladesh. But in the West one had to be careful about one's behaviour in public. I left the theatre feeling somewhat disappointed at the loss of opportunity.

After the film, fresh with the exploits of Whoopi Goldberg, we walked to his house, a modest dwelling in the Asian part of the town, where he introduced me to his mother. She knew no Hindi or English and I do not speak Bengali, so we couldn't really communicate, except through Khalid. I could see he was not too comfortable having me there, and wanted me to take my leave as quickly as possible. His mother wanted me to stay on for dinner, but my vegetarianism provided a convenient excuse for they had prepared fish. So she brought out some cakes, and Khalid was quick to point out that she had made them with her own hands. Then I got up to go, mumbling a scarcely audible 'namaste' which he objected to, wanting me to say 'salaam wallikum'. I had to try it out thrice before I got it right; his mother was amused.

Khalid walked me a part of the way to the restaurant, up to the George Eliot Road. For once, despite his warm fishy blood I saw him shivering, and felt concerned. I asked him to buy a fur coat like the one I had, but he said it would cost a hundred pounds, which, roughly, were his wages for the week. When I promised him one on his birthday, which was next month, he smiled and said I was lonely, he would get me married!

5

'I fancy you,' I blurted out to him at last. It was in the smoke-filled kitchen when no one was present. He was peeling onions and there were tears in his eyes. At first he pretended not to understand. 'I have sex with women, not with men,' he retorted, sniffing. Then he stopped talking to me completely. Days passed: his lips were stitched. When he had to speak, to find out, say, how many naans I wanted, he spoke very rudely, and threw the naans into my plate. Thus spake my diary: Knew my disclosure would have that kind of effect. I'm the sinner, you see, incarnation of the devil. Worried he might tell on me.

Seeing me in the dumps but not quite knowing why, Ahmed at once came to my rescue. He put me in his car and drove to a brothel where he said I'd find the loveliest of European girls. Small girls, big girls. Blondes and brunettes. He couldn't understand it when I spurned his offer. 'I'm just missing home, that's all,' I said, as he insisted on finding out the reason for my mood. I told him to drive back to the restaurant. 'Think of us, we've been away from our motherland for years,' he grumbled, taking a U-turn and accelerating, and stopping outside some other Indian restaurant. I read his thoughts: why was I seen so often in the company of his nephew and employee, when he, the owner of the restaurant, was nearer my age and status?

I was now Khalid's enemy. The naans were still thrown into my plate, but that was our only contact. I began going down for dinner very late, usually after ten, when the place was packed with customers and everyone was busy, and came up immediately after my meal. Khalid's off days were now a relief, I felt much better when he wasn't there. Once or twice I said 'hi' to him as he was occupied with sundry chores, but he did not respond. I got it: he wanted to see, hear and speak no evil.

When they finally closed the restaurant for the night, cleaned up and left, and I was alone again, I would sneak into Khalid's room and examine it. The dressing-table had cigarette butts scattered on it. His clothes were everywhere: shirts, trousers, underpants. Sometimes, I picked up his underpants, sniffed them and masturbated. That was therapeutic.

Then I apologized. 'I'm sorry if I offended you,' I said one night as he came up to smoke. He was silent for a while. Then, 'We all make mistakes,' he pronounced, his face very grim. 'So why don't you speak to me?' I persisted. 'No time sir,' he shot back.

Suddenly he offered me a cigarette. I said I would accept it only if he made it up with me. He undid his fly and fiddled with his underwear.

The next day he asked me what I would like for dinner. I said cauliflower, but he served me brinjals. He was eating an ice cream, and left it unfinished to prepare my meal. (Since England is a fridge, this is okay.) As I ate, he kept asking me how the food was, eager to hear it was good, and although it wasn't as divine as the stuff dished up by his uncle, I praised it to the skies. When he touched the frying pan and burnt himself, I helped him wash his hands in a basin of cold water.

But who had won? He had cleverly manipulated me into being his friend once again, as any other male might be, and such a platonic relationship was now unacceptable to me. 'I thought of you as my older brother,' he said to me around this time, in a tone that reeked of betrayal, and I dismissed it as incestuous rubbish. So when he tried the food trick again, bringing me some chicken dhansak to taste for the salt, I refused, saying I had vowed never to touch meat. I also discouraged his visits to my room, for he was not prepared to sit and chat, not till I'd got that 'unclean' thing out of my mind. We had thus reached a stalemate. Even his birthday came and passed off uneventfully: I merely wished him and asked half-heartedly for a party, to which he ungraciously replied that Muslims didn't believe in parties. They had one every Friday!

6

At last the countdown began: in ten days I would leave England—and Khalid. I came back from the university with a large suitcase loaded with books, which he offered to haul up the stairs for me. He looked happy that evening. His father had unexpectedly arrived from Bangladesh. 'What did your father get you from home?' I asked. He made a face and explained that his father had fled from the police and come to England as a refugee.

The day after Christmas, Khalid did not report for work. Ahmed was justified in chafing because the week between Christmas and New Year is always the busiest for restaurants. I quietly instigated him to phone the fellow and summon him: these last few days I wanted him near me all the time. But he wasn't at home, according to his mother. Ahmed asked her to send him to the restaurant as soon as he returned. My eyes were fastened on the door, and every time someone gave it a push, my heart quivered. But Khalid never appeared that night. I went to bed hungry and downcast.

It was on the next day, when there were barely forty-eight hours left for my departure, that Khalid finally realized I was leaving. He sat by my side as I had my dinner, neglecting his orders, and said he suffered from racial prejudice in England; that he would definitely come to Bombay and ask me to show him all the film stars' houses.

And when on New Year's Eve, amidst all the fanfare on the streets and in the restaurant, he came up to greet me as I was giving the finishing touches to my packing, he hugged me uninhibitedly. I was in the toilet shitting when he came, and he drummed on the door and asked what I was doing inside for so long. 'What does one do in the toilet?' I exclaimed. Afterwards he sat on a chair close to me, and I kissed him on the mouth. Then he unzipped, took out his stout, pink, circumcised cock, and allowed me to suck. The New Year was ushered in.

7

1 January is my last day in Britain. Khalid accepts the twenty-pound note I give him and serves me my last supper before I board the Flightlink Coach to Heathrow. The meal is made up of brinjals, and he tells me of a brinjal that, when cut open, was found to have had the words 'Allah-u-Akbar' inscribed on it. Then he launches into a sort of harangue on Islam, repeating the things he's heard from the imams at prayer meetings on Fridays. When he talks about the tortures of hell, I suggest that in spite of its drawbacks, it is an exciting place. He does not agree; holds that the followers of all other faiths are infidels and bastards.

I finish my meal and wash my hands. The taxi arrives. On Ahmed's instructions, Khalid helps me stuff my luggage in the boot, but before the taxi starts he hurries back to the restaurant. His naans are burning in the tandoori oven.

A Mermaid Called Aida

A Review

After the success of his very first documentary *Nadia—the Fearless* which was a fine tribute to this amazing woman of yesteryears' Indian screen who did all her extraordinary stunts herself (today's hero/ heroines please note), Wadia was on the lookout for another subject.

In January 1996 as he sunbathed in Goa, Wadia had the pleasure of meeting a fabulous transsexual—Aida Banaji. As he delved into her real story he made a new friend and found the subject for his new documentary, *A Mermaid Called Aida*.

Rizwan Gubitra, also keen to produce a film on transsexuals, joined forces with Wadia. They then interviewed Aida on camera over a three-day, eight-hour session. Family and friends who were interviewed refused to be on film and perforce Wadia had to create prototype characters to reflect their mindsets. On the screen, it is Aida herself as she is today who tells the story (along with inputs by raconteurs who represent the people in her life) of her traumatic childhood and adolescence. This method of narration leads to some confusion, specially as to the time sequences.

The documentary attempts to unravel the harrowing struggles of a child born as Adi Banaji, to fulfil his desire to become a woman. The boy, Adi, loved to dress up as a girl and was allowed to do so but only at home. Around the age of six, whilst playing 'doctor-doctor' he discovered that he was different from the other girls and was promptly thrown out of their circle. He still liked to play with them and shunned rough boyish games. Around the age of thirteen, he had 'bumps' under his nipples. He desperately hoped that he was going to be a girl.

Fascinated by an article on transsexuals that he came across in *Playboy* magazine, Adi followed this up by clandestine research from his father's medical books. At the age of sixteen or seventeen he fell in love with a Greek sailor and would have run away with him if he had not been stopped by his parents. Now, emotionally fragile, unable to study, he was allowed to work in his father's office. Here he met a boy from Bahrain and had a torrid love affair with him, unknown to his parents, for almost six years. A chance remark by his father that since Adi was such a sensitive boy he should try to be a spiritual medium made him try automatic writing (a psychic exercise in which the writing is telepathically dictated), which found him a lover from a former life!

The desire to be a woman and remove all the hair from his body made Adi personally burn out each hair follicle by electrolysis—an excruciatingly painful process. His father now seemed to understand the complexities of his son's mind. He wanted to send Adi to Germany for a transsexual operation and let him stay on there with relatives. His mother disagreed violently and battles between father and mother followed. Then suddenly his father died, the German trip was cancelled and the boy from Bahrain left him. Totally traumatized, Adi's suicide attempt failed.

One does not know why he did not seek psychiatric help. Also the film does not make it clear when he started undergoing plastic surgery. Silicone breast implants, changing of hairlines, ear, nose and jaw 'jobs' followed. After one of the silicone implants, the stitches gave way, and the implant slipped out and resulted in massive bleeding. This was narrated by Aida herself very casually: 'The surgeon slipped it in again and stitched me up.' Now at least he looked like a woman but was not one. The penultimate step had to be taken. The penis had to be replaced by the vagina.

Adi got more confidence after his meeting with another transsexual—Farah Rustom. After a series of operations (the details of which brought home the fact that all this was an expensive, painful and long drawn out process) extending over three years or more, Aida has now got a clitoris. Not everyone can spare so many years, spend so much money and bear so much pain. But today, the boy Adi is the fabulously glamorous Aida—a woman in all respects except the ability to bear children. And she is going to get married!

What director Wadia has so courageously portrayed on the screen is the true story of a woman trapped in a man's body—'a venus with a penis', says Aida. At the end of the screening, glamorous Aida herself appeared on stage to confidently answer questions put to her by a slightly dazed audience. I left the auditorium with the hope that Aida had at last found herself.

from Parsiana, *December 1996*

from Waiting for Winter

Belinder Dhanoa

Hans notices little about his bride-to-be, consumed as he is by the sorrow of seeing his father sick and dying. He loves his father intensely. His pain is magnified by the knowledge that the old man's death will mean the end of the one enduring relationship in his life. He is familiar with his mother's face only through her photographs and with her beauty and accomplishments through the stories of her old ayah whom he cannot entirely believe.

'I remember her a little,' Hans's elder sister Prema says. 'She had this very husky voice. She spoke so low you'd have to lean towards her to hear the words. It sort of invited intimacy and gentleness. Even father's voice assumed a softness when he spoke to her. She named us you know. Prema and Hans. Everyone said they were strange names for Sikh children but she didn't care. She had her way. It was very difficult to disagree with her then as her attitude would become so hurt—wounded—that you'd begin to feel guilty, like some horrible bullying aggressor. And before you began to hate yourself completely, you'd have to give in to her.

'That's what I remember. Then she died. You were barely three. And I went off to live with maasiji until I'd finished school. I felt quite orphaned then you know. At least you had father.'

With his mother dead Hans finds his father's presence emphasized. Gurbax Singh, endowed with a wide spectrum of emotions, is generous in giving his son affection when it does not interfere with wielding the discipline he sees as essential for the growing boy.

Hans accepts both affection and authority. Seeing through his admiring childishness—a promise of his own future in his father's dynamic masculinity.

He does not recall his years at the boys' boarding school as oppressive. He remembers it as a time of light. Of the discovery of the joys of reading. He remembers it as the time of friendships—born and destroyed by a single gesture of sharing or forgetfulness. Tumultuous. High-pitched. When even the moments of being alone were the consummation of a fierce desire. A battle to tear oneself away from beloved companions and enticing pastimes. And so, more precious.

He returns home for a holiday. He is fourteen.

His father pinches his chin and turns his face to the light pouring in through the open window.

'As pale as a young girl. We'll send him back a man this time, eh Billu?' Hans turns briefly to smile at Billu, the nineteen-year-old son of their estate manager. Then he grasps his father's wrist in his narrow hand and moves it away from his face.

'You will find me more of a man than you suspect, Father. If you care to try me now.'

Gurbax is delighted. He hugs his son against his massive chest.

'See how the young cock crows! Take him now. Out into the open. See how far his voice carries.'

Billu looks at Hans while he answers the older man.

'Yes. I'll take him now. Out in the open. There's so much I can teach him.'

Hans laughs. 'Really? Like what?'

'How to ride a motorcycle, for instance. I can teach you that. Can't I?'

Hans' voice emerges in a thin whistle of excitement. 'Yes. Now, teach me now. I will learn. I must. Father?'

Gurbax Singh is laughing. 'Yes, you must. But only on

the farm roads. You will not go onto any public road. Do you understand?'

'Yes.' The two answer simultaneously.

They laugh. All three of them. For no apparent reason.

Billu explains the mechanics of the motorcycle to Hans before he allows him to touch it. When he is satisfied with Hans' understanding they go out for a ride.

The dust rises behind them in a cylindrical haze. The air is a sparkling gold that shines on their bare exulting skin.

Billu drives fast. And then faster. With Hans goading him on he goes through the fields, racing over the bumpy surface.

When he stops, Hans can barely support his own weight on his trembling legs.

They are near a well. Billu draws out a bucketful of water and throws it over Hans—who screams with the abandon of a wild animal.

'It's cold. It's hot. I mean the water's cold. The sun is hot. I don't know what I mean and I don't care.'

He screams again. A shrill wordless sound that makes Billu wince.

'There. Now you can tell Father how far my voice carries.'

'Take off your clothes and hang them out. The sun will dry them in minutes.' Billu takes off his own wet shirt and hooks it onto the branch of a tree. Water drips from his hair into his eyes. He kneels beside Hans, who is sitting, legs stretched out, his back resting against the tree. 'Feel this.' He takes Hans's hand and places it on his flat stomach. 'All muscle. Every inch of my body as hard as iron. Here. Feel. My back. Shoulders. Touch here. Did you know you could have muscles like this on your thighs? A man's body can be wonderful. So full of power. Do you think I'm very vain? Your hands are soft. And so cool.'

He stops Hans's moving hand with his own.

'You are so—so clean. Like shining silver. Delicate. A glittering fish slipping through the clear waters of a shallow pond. See how rough my hand is against your skin.'

And he slips his hand under the elastic waistband of Hans's underpants. The two boys crouch. Their faces on level, looking into each other's eyes. 'You knew. Somehow you knew what I wanted,' Billu says. Still holding Hans.

'Yes. Yes,' Hans says impatiently. Then he laughs and rolls over.

Billu falls with him. And they wrestle in the dust. Laughing until they are weak and gasping, covered with mud and dirt.

Billu is the first to recover. He carries the bucket of water to Hans under the tree and begins to wash him. Hans, unresisting, smiles. When he has finished, Billu throws a bucket of water over himself and drags on his clothes over his wet body.

'Time to go back.' He stands by the motorcycle.

Hans walks towards him buttoning his shirt. His eyes looking firectly into Billu's eyes. He stands still. Facing him for a split second. And then puts his right hand on the back of Billu's neck and pulls his head down.

Billu is puzzled, a little nervous.

'Just one moment,' Hans says.

With the tip of his smooth pink tongue he traces the outline of Billu's lips. And with a swift fluid movement he sucks the moisture from his mouth.

'Son-of-a-bitch!' Billu's shout is sheer surprise. 'Where did you learn that?'

Hans shrugs. With a hint of arrogance.

'Let's go. Come on let's go. Let's go.'

They become lovers under the tree, lighted by the strong yellow glow of the afternoon sun.

'I love you,' Hans declares one day. 'Do you know that?'

Billu laughs in genuine amusement.

'You don't love me,' he says. 'You love the pleasure that I give you.'

His hands continue to move. Kneading gently, insistently, on the inside of Hans's thigh.

'And you don't love me? You love only the pleasure that I give you?'

Hans teases, disbelieving.

He throws himself against Billu and begins to kiss his face. Billu tries to push him away, both giggling. Until he is silenced by Hans's tongue pressing against his own. And he is aroused to passion.

'Your mouth is like the flesh of a ripe guava. Sweet and soft. With a taste of wildness.'

'And you say you don't love me?'

'I love you. I love you as a brother.'

Hans is satisfied.

The time for Hans to go back to school comes close.

'You'll always be here when I come back,' Hans commands.

'No. The next time you come home I'll be in college. In Delhi. You won't remember all this. Forget it.'

'Why do you always talk like that? It's stupid.' Fury stretches the skin taut around his eyes and mouth. 'Will you forget?'

'Yes I will.' Billu smiles honestly. 'I'll find myself a girlfriend in Delhi. I'll choose one with nice big boobs and a juicy red mouth.'

Hans grows cold with disgust.

'In that case I don't think we should bother with each other any more. Don't touch me,' he snaps as Billu reaches out.

'Don't sulk, Hans. Come on now. We have just a few days left. Together. Don't be a baby.'

'I'm not the baby. You are. At least I know what I want.'

'Don't spoil everything. Come here.'

'I don't want you to touch me.'

'Of course you do,' Billu laughs.

He pulls Hans into his arms and kisses his ear.

'You're a greedy little bastard.'

He caresses Hans' throat as they lie against each other.

'You'll understand one day. All this. What is happening

with you and me. It passes. The real thing is when it happens with a woman.'

'Has it happened to you? With a woman?'

'No. But it will. I'll make sure it does. Soon.' He smiles to himself.

'And do you think she'll be able to kiss you quite like this? Or touch you like this? Or make your fucking prick reach out for the sky—like this?'

Billu gasps and then yelps as Hans's vicious fingers pinch suddenly at his naked flesh.

'You arrogant little shit. You . . .'

But Hans knows how to silence him.

'We're finished now,' Hans declares when they are dressed. 'You can go and find yourself a woman for all I care. I don't need you. And I won't need a woman. Ever.'

'Whatever you say. You're the boss.'

'Don't sneer at me. I know. Why would I waste myself on a woman? I think you're a fool. You're losing. Somewhere.'

'You don't know what you're saying. You're just a kid. I suppose I never should have done this to you.'

Hans's voice is frozen with a stubborn pride.

'Don't flatter yourself into believing you've "done" anything to me. You leave me as you found me—untouched.'

Billu shrugs.

'Well, whatever you do—just keep this whole thing to yourself. Okay? Half the country may spend its time fucking the other half. But nobody likes it shouted from the rooftops.'

He shakes his head slowly in a gesture of regret.

'And remember. It's normal to give it to a woman. What we're doing—you and I—to each other is just buggering.'

'I won't forget.'

*

The passion stays with him. Directing his life in ways he would never have thought possible. Driving him to find his pleasures where his fastidious sensibilities revolt. Building in him a self-disgust which he holds a dark secret.

When his father expresses a desire to see him married he sees it as an opportunity to attempt a rejection of his present life. He wonders—was Billu right after all? But there is no conviction in the thought. He agrees to a marriage to please his father. To promise the dying man a continuation of the bloodline.

Underground

R. Raj Rao

You belong with the . . .
It can't be said.
As in the old days
the touch of some men polluted,
today it's yours, viruses and all.
But goo has its uses.
Consider the ripe harvest
along the railway lines opposite Dharavi
fertilized by defecating humans,
and goo, strong on smell,
has the power of ammunition
to trigger off memories
of a long forgotten lover
met in an underground urinal.

The Underground has its own shades.
In London it's the metro railroad
with poems on the walls,
and back in Bombay
it's the mafia world
of nightly blackmailers.
But tube or dark tunnel,
its fault-lines are anal,
harking back to painful passages
of seismic prose,

Lakshman Gaikwad read on a train journey.
The Underground is where you belong,
while the city buzzes overhead,
ghost-shit on your tongue.
You undress underground
and find your Garden of Eden,
Eden Gardens abounding in Adams and serpents:
Raju, 19, office boy at Bora Bazaar,
Gulab, 22, waiter at Satkar,
Pandu, 50, coolie at VT.

You stand in your stall
and look over the wall.
One comes up,
seizes you by the shirt,
demands money and bottles of beer
for friends outside.
As the saying goes,
in the company of friends, death is a nuptial feast.

You want to throw loo goo on his face.
But you give in meekly,
handing over cash and valuables.
The meek shan't inherit.
You stand bereft,
the city your headload.

Opinions

R. Raj Rao

Onions and opinions come cheap in Bombay.

The Gujaratis in the neighbourhood
want to know why you're still single,
though eligible.
They don't understand it when you tell them
you're married three times over,
divorced once.
How come there are no children in the flat,
they enquire,
no evidence of vegetable curries cooking.

Shantabai
who comes once a day
to wash your undies
goes one step further.
She thinks
a man without wife and kids
is cremated by the Bombay Municipal
                        Corporation
upon death.

You wonder whether she's making a pass.

Bomgay

R. Raj Rao

Family members
from England, America and Canada
visit you at Bombay
which they call Bomgay.
Some of them are sex tourists,
you their post-colonial pimp
hungry for pounds and dollars.

Religiously, you take them
on a conducted tour
that includes Gokul, Voodoo and ARK
               headquarters.

But what pleases them most,
more than even the gents' toilet
on platform number two of Dadar Station WR,
is Apsara theatre's steeple.
God's own penis mightier than the sword,
pointing menacingly towards the sky.

*(These three poems are among the six poems on which the
film* Bomgay, *produced by Riyad Wadia, was based.)*

Beta

Rakesh Ratti

Mummy keeps her jewels
in a box full of dreams,
dreams that will be realized
in the echoes of my screams.

Father waits for the day
I bring a crimson bride
yet if I sit on a white horse
it'll be an empty ride.

Every chapter of my life
written by their hands,
if I now reach for the pen
will they understand?

Should I listen to my heart
and wrestle with this guilt?
Should I lock myself inside
the walls they would build?

I want to fill their eyes with joy,
yet let my spirit run wild.
How can I find the love I seek
And still remain their child?

Sunshine Trilogy

Owais Khan

I. TALKING TO THE SUNSHINE

I get tired of journeys
I get tired of my job.
Of driving
of being driven
crazy by my mother's demands.
I get tired of seasons;
of summer, of winter
even, of monsoons.
I get tired
of conforming to the society's diktats.
I get tired
of screaming queens
of scheming activists.
I get tired of my desire
for sexy boys with massive dicks.
I, often, even get tired
of myself.

What I never
seem to get tired of
is talking to you.
Anytime, any place;
with you, without you;

I can talk, and talk forever
to you.
Sometimes,
I talk in prose
sometimes in third class
poetry like this.
Sometimes in the surreal
language of the dreams.
And sometimes without talking at all.

You are my life
my sunshine,
how could I get tired
of being with you . . .

II. A POSER . . .

I am not the wittiest
of queens you can find.
I do not have
the sexiest of bodies
which keep flitting around you.
I certainly do not possess
the biggest of penile appendages
that you have experienced.
I am not even
passable as a pleasure provider.
I am so much older,
with so much excess fat,
with so little time
before I lose the last hair on my head.
I have the loveliest of tempers—
and the worst of possessive natures.

Given half a chance
my mom would exchange
me for an Idi Amin.

So why do I try wooing you,
my Sunshine?
What could you possibly
find in me?

III. . . . AND A REPLY

He told me
all about himself.
What he perhaps thought,
warts, and all.
And asked me not
an iota in return.

And he watched my face
bit by bit revealing
his innermost,
perhaps, waiting,
for the first signs
of flinching in my face.

Little did he know
that in exchange of being his,
I could give up
all that is mine,
and all that,
could ever be mine.
Least of all,
ever think of insisting
that he fall in line
with the established mores of

the present day society.

Little did he know
that riddled with my numerous
insecurities and infirmities,
I could scarcely believe
that he had
actually brought with him
for me
his golden sunshine
flooding all the darkest
deepest corners of my being
with his undying rays of love.

My Sunshine,
would you actually believe
that the most cherished,
the most beloved,
the most important moment
in my entire life,
is when
in a reply to my most
convoluted question about us,
you had buried your face
in my naked shoulder, and
had said, simply,
'I want to
be yours.'

from Trying to Grow

Firdaus Kanga

Cyrus came around lunchtime, kissed Dolly, said, 'I knew I didn't stand a chance,' mumbled at me, 'I've got to rush, have a lunch date,' and was gone.

I was sure he was meeting Ruby. When he didn't come that night I was certain. Then I wondered if I'd hurt him last night by not saying thank you. I was terrified I'd never see him again.

Cyrus didn't turn up the next evening or the next or . . . I woke about sixty-five times every night, opened my book on the Indian Contract Act and sobbed into the passages Cyrus had marked. Or I sat at the window and watched the stars because they reminded me of the telescope. The day I spent in a night-black fog, looking at plastic bags and Sam's razor with a speculative eye. I cursed Ruby, because I bet if she hadn't been around to entice him, Cyrus would have got over his hurt if only because he'd have wanted someone to talk to. I could see his firm hands in her hair and his arcing mouth mocking kisses into her neck and I had to pull down the shutters on my mind. And think of other things.

Like Dolly was going away really soon, as soon as Sam got his visa and stuff. Because there was no way Salim could come to Bombay for the next two years and even Sera thought thirty wasn't exactly young to get married. So the plan was for Dolly to fly out to New York with Sam, on her last free tickets, and get married there.

We thought it was absolutely right for Dolly to take Sam

along instead of her mother because she was always his daughter like I was Sera's son. That's how it is with almost every family I know. Both parents are crazy about both kids but in some tiny way each adopts one—a kind of division of labour. I don't know how it works for people who have more than two kids because Parsis almost never do. They feel it's some sort of extravagance, like having a television in the bedroom.

At last Cyrus came over. 'Hello!' he said with his killing smile. 'Sorry I've been neglecting you.'

'You shouldn't be,' I said, taking deep, slow breaths. 'You come because you like being with me, not to give me company. At least, I hope it's that way.'

'Brit,' he said, falling into his familiar cross-legged seat in front of me, 'have I . . . hurt you?'

'No.' I thought how easy it would be to fall off my chair, right into his arms.

'I know it's been—how many, ten, eleven days?' Twelve, I thought, and you didn't even keep count. 'But I've been busy; really, I have.'

'Of course; you don't have to give me an account.'

'Fucking shit! Stop that!'

'Don't shout at me, Cyrus.'

'Okay, so I didn't meet you, so you feel awful. I'd have felt miserable if you'd stopped meeting me suddenly. Why can't you say so? What's happened to your famous frankness?' His face turned a darker brown and, if his skin was finding trouble holding in that blood, his eyes were thrown open to make more room.

'Cyrus?' I whispered. Then I was lifted off my chair and he was saying into my hair, 'Brit, I'm sorry, but will you promise never, never to stop—'

'Stop what, Cyrus?' My hand was on his neck and I was rubbing his earlobe with my thumb.

'Being my friend. Because I never will, not even if you never will, I mean, never do, I mean never—' We started laughing louder and louder as if someone was turning a knob in our chests.

Then I realized I had a huge hard-on pushing into his tummy, and the way he was holding me around my back, there was no way I could move away without falling out of his arms. And there was no way I could turn soft as long as I could smell his clean hard smell and see his small nostrils flare with the effect of carrying me. I kissed his eyelids and he smiled, so I kissed the drooping corners of his mouth. Then I shut my eyes and held him for every moment that had passed since he asked for that safety-pin.

I could've stayed that way till Sera crew the morning open but Cyrus had shifted his mouth to mine and begun sucking with small milky sounds. I opened my mouth to the bristle of his stubble and the gush of hot breath from his nose while I felt his big man's hands grasping my bottom.

My hard-on was melting away and I didn't know what to do. I mean here I was on the brink of passion and all I could think of was that I didn't want Cyrus's toothpaste-tasting tongue in my mouth where it was slowly pushing its way past my transparent teeth. Somehow it felt all wrong as if I had clasped the wrong partner in the dark.

I gagged and Cyrus drew his head back and said, 'Sorry, this isn't working.'

'Not for me either,' I said, feeling my sovereign mouth with my tongue. I shook my head and felt his warm face with my fingertips. A huge tenderness was lapping against my insides, a sea of semen and tears.

'Are you gay?' he said, at last.

'I don't know, I don't know,' I said. 'I look at you now and I want you, and I'm angry with myself for feeling what I did when you were holding me. As if I was one of a pair of Siamese twins—'

'Um, I know; we're much too alike, aren't we, stubble and muscles.' He put me down on the large carved sofa and sat on the floor in front of me.

'Don't do that,' I said wearily. 'Oh, what I thought it would be—'

'Well, at least I didn't have any expectations,' he said, grinning.

'Then why did you?' I said. I knew why I did. But my reasons couldn't have been his; as clear as I could see he had no reason to want me.

'I knew you wanted me.'

'You tried to make love to me out of charity?' I shouted.

'Sshh! You want to wake them up? It wasn't charity, you ass. I wanted to because I knew you wanted me like crazy.'

'You knew? All along?'

'Sure. The way you'd stare and stare at my crotch.' He began to laugh, watching me all the time.

'D'you really mean that?' I was feeling what I later found out was drunk.

'Of course. How do you think I knew? And that neck massage you gave me? Oh, boy! I'll never—'

'Okay, so what if I wanted you?'

'You know what it's like to be wanted that much?'

'Of course not, you idiot.'

'There's no need to get angry when you're sad.'

'You know, I really love you.'

'Why did you want me, Brit?'

I'd rehearsed this about sixty-seven times. 'You're tall, I'm four feet nothing, you've got muscles in your thighs when I've got matchsticks, you have a voice like hot chocolate—'

'Stop being funny.'

'I'm not. You have got a voice like hot chocolate and osteo makes me squawk. You've got a swimmer's chest; I've got a pigeon-chest. Girls love your body; they don't look at mine except to shudder—'

'That's not true. No one thinks about that, once they know you.'

'You look good and not all the cosmetic surgeons in America can make me like looking at myself.'

'Is any of that important?'

'Don't tell me beauty is skin deep and all that crap

because it isn't true. I want to be straight and tall because I've got just one life and I'll go through it without anyone ever wanting me like I wanted you. It's like—'

'A sweeper watching a Brahmin?'

'Yes, you either hate that something you can never have, or you adore it.'

'Tell me more.'

'The desire of the moth for the star.'

'That doesn't explain lust.'

'It does. If I could have you, which meant you wanted me, that meant my body was as good as yours.'

'Whoo!' he gasped, spreading his palm on his chest, letting his tongue hang out. That tongue.

'Wait,' I said, 'you haven't heard everything.' My passion had escaped solitary confinement and it couldn't stop talking. 'I was opting out of the race—'

'For girls?'

'Yes.' I made a face like that chap in *MAD* magazine.

'But you were entering another race, weren't you?'

'You were out of reach. So where was the race?'

'. . . but I wasn't out of reach, was I?'

'As soon as you weren't I got out of your arms. Don't look like that, I'm not crazy. It's just that wanting you was a faking, wasn't it?'

'That hard-on was no fake; everything you wanted to do with me wasn't. What the hell, Brit—this fucking frigidity, where's it going to get you?'

'But don't you see! I couldn't do things with you because it would have been like a poor girl marrying a millionaire for his money. You'd say that was sick, wouldn't you?'

'That girl never felt for him what you felt for me.'

'Feeling, feeling, tell me, what's the use of feeling?' Do all men sound like their mothers when things get tough? 'I've felt sorry for myself, and frightened for myself, and what good has that done me? You've got to know what makes you feel something.'

'By which time love is desiccated—'

'It was never love.'

'Are you sure, Brit?'

I looked at his solemn face, his mouth turned down at the corners, eyes large with what I was feeling, and I knew I wasn't sure. I didn't answer him.

He smiled and put his warm hand on my knee. 'You are looking for something, Brit. Will you be brave enough to grab it when you find it?'

'I don't know, I don't know, I don't know,' I said, answering that other question.

'Stop it,' he barked in George Patton style. 'Stop looking like Osteo Brit. Think of the problems you'll never have—'

'Waiting in a bus queue with smelly fishmongers—'

'Squelching your way through monsoon slush on your way to work—'

'Getting pickpocketed in a crowd—'

'Being knocked over by a speeding taxi—'

'Wearing out my shoes—'

'Helping with the housework when the servants are on strike—'

'You never did that, I bet. Your mother wouldn't let you, and Defarge wouldn't dare.'

'I have problems you never will,' he said, trying to look like Saint Joan and ending up like the Dauphin.

'Like?' I said sceptically.

'Wanting someone because they want you. That's one of the reasons why I sleep around. If a girl wants me really badly. God! It's so exciting I can't resist.'

'What about what you want?'

'Sometimes I wonder.'

'But you were ready to go gay.'

'I wanted to know what it would be like—you've got to try everything once.'

'That's cheap.'

'That's brave.'

'Wanting a girl just because she wants you—that's not brave. Just shows you're terrified of never being wanted again. Like I felt with Ruby after I missed that kiss.'

'Ruby! God! She's something!'

'Take care you don't get her preggers,' I said.

'Preggers? Ha, he! Where did you get that forties' phrase from!'

'Sera—she thought Dolly was preggers.'

'Dolly's going away *soon*, isn't she?'

'Will you take me around and things?'

Cyrus bit his lip. 'I'll try my best but I'm going to be a bit busy—'

'I understand,' I said, swinging away on a trapeze and my brave act. 'I'll only ask when it's absolutely necessary.'

'Very funny. Brit, look! Just because I can't spend so much time with you doesn't mean I don't want to. I just want to do something else too.'

'Sure, you don't have to worry about me.' A cock crew from the servant's quarters of the building behind us, where we'd seen the bathing bai.

'Four o'clock! Sera's going to slaughter me if she wakes. I'm going. Put me in my chair.' I was thinking of the time when Sam had found me Cyrus-drunk in the rocking chair.

'Okay, here goes!' He swung me into his arms. 'Take care you don't get another hard-on. You know what that does to me.'

'What!' screamed Sera. 'Am I going mad? Or did I hear right?'

'Fucking shit!'

'What!'

'Put me down,' I said through my teeth, realizing my hands were clasping Cyrus's bottom because his arms had sagged with shock.

'Sure,' he said, letting me down gently.

'Are the two of you perverted?' said Sera.

'It was all a joke,' said Cyrus, flashing his Sera-stumping smile.

'I don't think so,' said Sera, trying to keep her voice from flying out of the window. 'Defarge told me how she found you in the bathroom one night, some time back. I didn't pay any attention because I know her imagination is as dirty as those books they sell at Flora Fountain. But I was wrong.'

'Look,' I said, 'do you really think we're lovers? Do you think a guy like Cyrus would want a guy like me? We're not even the same size.'

'Aaahah!' said Sera, clapping a hand to her mouth. 'How d'you know what size he is? You've seen him, haven't you?'

'Not that size, Sera,' said Cyrus. 'This size—look.' He stretched an imaginary tape-measure from my hair to my slippers.

'Then what were you doing in each other's arms?'

'I was lifting him into his chair.'

'Brit doesn't need to be lifted into his chair. All you have to do is move the chair over to him and he shifts into it by himself. You've known him long enough to know that. You are perverted—both of you.'

'Well,' said Cyrus, the smartass, 'you need two hands to clap.'

'Saaaam,' howled Sera.

'Yes, darling,' Sam stepped out from behind the door, where he was awaiting his cue.

'Our son is a pervert.' She dropped her words with the dull thud of paperweights.

'Homosexual, you mean,' said Sam. 'No one is a pervert any more. You can slice up half a dozen women and you're only socially maladjusted.'

'I'm not gay!' I shouted in panic. 'At least, I don't think so,' I added, not as loudly.

'Nor am I, if you want the truth,' said Cyrus.

'Of course they aren't,' shouted Dolly from her bed. 'They drool over *Playboy* magazine and that has pictures of naked girls.'

Sera looked at Sam doubtfully. Sam nodded and smiled back. I blessed their innocence.

'Why were they in each other's arms?' said Sera, shaking her white head.

'Okay, I'll tell you why,' I said, smiling like Hercule Poirot in the last chapter of an Agatha Christie. 'I'm giving up law.'

'But you've hardly started, lad.'

'Isn't that good? I haven't wasted too much time.'

'No!' cried Sera. 'Please, Brit—no—it's bad enough Dolly's leaving us and now you—'

'What's the connection?'

'What are you going to do?'

'Write.'

'Hooray!' said Cyrus, raising me in his arms like a glass of champagne. I'd never, in my life, been so high. That should've told me where I was headed next.

from The Golden Gate

Vikram Seth

4.24

Phil looks at Ed: intense, athletic,
Silent—the sort of man whom he's
Uneasy with. But Ed's ascetic
Tension betrays his own unease;
And by now Phil's free-floating status
(Buoyed by spirituous afflatus)
Projects goodwill on all mankind—
And so, in half an hour, we find
The pair engaged in conversation,
Which, now that he's regained his cool
And half slipped back to playing the fool,
Revolves round Ed's prolonged narration
Of how he happened to procure
A green iguana from a store.

4.25

' . . . They had a sale on small iguanas—
Babies—a span long, kind of cute.
Sure, I'd gone in to buy piranhas,
But seeing them, I knew they'd suit
My image: I could take them walking

Through the Financial District, talking
To them about the price of gold.
We wouldn't make the centerfold
Of *Playgirl*, as they aren't too pretty,
But what the heck, I didn't care:
Traffic would swerve, and folks would stare
—I had it figured out—the city
Would halt, the cops would come and say,
"Get those darn things out of the way!"

4.26

But, sadly, Arnold Schwarzenegger
—I got just one—looks really strange:
His legs keep getting bigger and bigger
But not his torso—Should I change
His food?' Ed asks with some disquiet.
'Don't know,' replies Phil. 'What's his diet?'
'Salads, and larvae—and bonemeal.'
'Why that?' asks Phil. 'Because I feel
His jaw's so rubbery and floppy
He may need extra calcium.' 'No.
The phosphorus-calcium ratio
Is far too high in bonemeal. Copy
My method: cut that bonemeal out,
And feed it vitamins till it's stout.

4.27

To feed it bonemeal is to maim it.'
'You've kept iguanas, Phil?' 'Oh, sure—
Iguanas, rabbits, dogs, you name it!
My wife—but I don't any more . . .

(Phil's speech grows slurred) . . . We got a spider—
Paul and I call it Easy Rider.'
'Who's Paul?' 'My son. He lives with me.'
Ed frowns at Phil: 'Why shouldn't he?'
'Oh! I'm divorced,' says Phil. 'You married?'
'No, no—' 'Well, don't! Women are turds.
That whole snake pit is . . . for the birds,'
Phil mutters—but his slurs have carried
To Jan, who with ferocious mien
Injects herself into the scene.

4.28

'Phil, you're obnoxious . . . (Like a razor
Her voice dissects him) . . . when you're drunk.'
Her eyes bore through him like a laser.
'What . . . ? What . . . ?' In an amnesic funk
'What did I say?' asks Philip (thinking,
That's Jan . . . she's pretty nice . . . likes drinking . . .
What's made her mad?) ' . . . Hey, have a drink—'
He offers her a glass. 'Men stink!'
Janet exclaims with tingling fury.
'You puke all over us, then say,
"What did I do?" file us away
As saint, virago, nag, slut, houri
Or household pet or household drudge—
God—Claire was right . . . ' Phil does not budge

4.29

From where Jan leaves him, rooted, staring.
He leans in foggy shock on Ed.
Then in a voice drunk and despairing:

'I'm plastered! What was it I said?'
'Nothing you meant. You're right. You're plastered.'
'I'm going . . . home . . . ' 'Unless you've mastered
The art of driving straight when drunk,
Once you're behind that wheel, you're sunk!
I'll drive you home. Come back tomorrow
To fetch—' 'I live near Stanford, Ed.'
'Oh . . . well, in that case, share my bed—
Just don't try driving!—You can borrow
My toothbrush too. Come on, let's go—
Good night, Liz—Bye, John—Homeward ho!'

4.30

They totter car-wards. Now Ed's driving
Toward his Spartan lodgings, where,
Within two minutes of arriving,
Stretched on the bed, Phil sees a chair
Piled high with shirts, a tennis racket,
A Bible, an unopened packet
Of guitar strings, a saxophone,
Shaving cream, razor and cologne . . .
A commentary on Aquinas
Rests on the floor, while on a shelf
Lies the august *Summa* itself,
Next to (in order) *Conquering Shyness*,
The Zen of Chess, *The Eightfold Way*,
Theories of Film, and the *Pensées*.

4.31

Phil looks around at Ed's housekeeping.
Ed yawns, and strips off shirt and shoes.

Silence outside. The iguana's sleeping.
This quiet grid of avenues
With red-flowered gum for decoration
Lies deep in slumber and sedation.
'It suits me, Phil. The flat's quite small,
But there's a garden, after all—
And a small pool for the iguana . . . '
Phil's bleary eyes rest on a bowl
Of fruit, a crucifix, a roll
Of film, a photograph of Lana
Turner, who smiles across the floor
At Holbein's sketch of Thomas More.

4.32

'My patron saint.' 'Which one?' Ed, grinning,
Says, 'Go to sleep!' and turns to pray.
He asks forgiveness for his sinning,
Gives thanks for the expended day,
Consigns his spirit to God's charity . . .
Now Philip, with exiguous clarity
And some bewilderment, sees Ed
Cross himself twice, then come to bed.
Lights out. Phil mumbles, 'What a party!
I really blew it then with Jan.
Ed, thanks a lot. I mean it, man—
I haven't yet met a Dorati
I didn't like . . . (Across the bed
He reaches out and touches Ed) . . .

4.33

. . . Good night.' Ed fears to answer. Trembling,
He moves his hand across the space
—What terrifying miles—assembling
His courage, touches Philip's face
And feels him tense up and go rigid.
'I'm sorry,' Ed says, in a frigid,
Half-choking voice, 'I thought you might—
I didn't mean—I mean—good night.'
Taut with a cataleptic tension
They lie, unspeaking. Phil thinks, 'Why
Be so uptight? He's a great guy.
I've never bothered with convention.
God! It's a year that I've been chaste . . . ,'
And puts his arm around Ed's waist.

4.34

Now, just as things were getting tenser,
And Ed and Phil were making love,
The imperial official censor
—Officious and imperious—drove
His undiscriminating panzer
Straight through the middle of my stanza.
Now, Gentle Reader, is it right
This swine should put my Muse to flight,
Rooting about among my pearly
Wisdom till he finds orts that he
Can gobble down with grunting glee?
Forgive me, Reader, if I'm surly
At having to replace the bliss
I'd hoped I could portray, with this.

4.35

I'll move the ménage to mañana,
But under protest. Saturday
Dawns bright and clear, and the iguana
—Fantastic dragon of green clay,
Great saurian from realms primeval!—
With scraping, scuffling, and upheaval
Bestirs himself now in his shed.
Ed yawns and half gets out of bed,
Returns and nuzzles Philip's shoulder,
Puts on his jeans, and goes to get
An avocado for his pet.
He says, 'Poor Schwarz. It's getting colder.
This heat's kaput. Tonight, instead,
You can sleep underneath the bed.'

4.36

The warty beast observes Ed coldly,
Stares at the green and mottled pear
He proffers. Noisily and boldly
He crawls towards him, unaware
Of the loose leash that Ed is holding.
Ed slips it round him, gently scolding:
'Now watch that dewlap—mind those spines—'
But Schwarzenegger undermines
All of Ed's efforts at persuasion
—By jerking, clawing—until he
Obtains his avocado. 'We
Are now prepared for an invasion.
Of our quiescent neighborhood.
You want a walk? . . . (The head bobs.) . . . Good!'

4.37

Ed leaves, upon the kitchen table,
A note: *Dear Phil, Please help yourself*
To breakfast. Sorry I'm not able
To make it. Coffee's on the shelf.
I'll be back soon. Ed and his lizard
Now do their rounds: a comely wizard
And his unsightly basilisk.
Behind, two neighbors' children risk
Utter and prompt annihilation
Should the familiar's fiendish eyes
Turn on them. 'You'll burn up,' Pam cries.
She quakes in fear and veneration.
'Coward!' says Gabrielle in a tone
Of scorn. 'You'll only turn to stone . . .

4.38

You scaredy cat!' Pam begins crying.
Swiftly the reptile eyes look back.
Gabrielle gasps. Pam, petrifying,
Awaits the fiery-tongued attack.
'Hello,' says Ed, 'meet my iguana,
Brought all the way from Ecbatana
In the mysterious land of Wales
For kids to stroke his shiny scales.'
Pam thaws to Ed's enlightened coaching:
'Here's how to pet the friendly beast.
He isn't slimy in the least.'
Pam frowns and touches him, reproaching
Her friend (who's having none of that)
With 'Yeah? Now who's a scaredy cat!'

4.39

Perfecting their aerobic labors,
Once more around the block they creep,
Greeted by mailmen and by neighbors.
When Ed returns, Phil's still asleep.
But, upon waking, to his credit,
He does not try to expunge or edit
—With, 'Geez, I had so much to drink
Last night, I really cannot think
What happened . . .'—what in fact transpired.
He smiles at Ed: 'Good morning.' 'Hi!
Coffee?' 'You bet.' Ed's somewhat shy.
'This coffee really gets you wired,'
Phil says. 'It's just like . . . (With a groan) . . .
Christ! Paul! Ed, may I use your phone?'

4.40

'Sure. Phil—if Paul has no objection—
Would you—I've got this weekend free . . . '
Phil dials, nods, gets the connection.
'Joan? This is Phil. Is Paul—I see—
I'll wait . . . Hi, son, how are things going?—
Chuck's baseball cap? Great!—So they're showing
What? *Star Wars*? No, I can't allow—
Now, young man, don't you teach me how . . .
Paul! Did you hear me? *Star Wars*—Never!—
I don't care what she lets him do—
What's that? Chuck will make fun of you?—
Well, just this once then—But don't ever . . .
(Alas! that such Affected Tricks
Should flourish in a Child of Six!)

4.41

... You're welcome—You're a tricky fellow—
Does Monday suit you?—You don't care? ...
(Phil laughs) ... You're having fun!—Don't bellow:
It sounds worse than a madhouse there—
See you then, son—No, nothing, staying
With a friend—Ed—yeah, that's right, playing! ...
(Phil shakes his head) ... Now give the phone
To Mrs Lamont ... Hello there, Joan.
Thanks for all this—Not Sunday, Monday,
Yes, after school—Yes, he can see
Star Wars—Say hi to Matt for me!—
That's very kind. I hope that one day
I can take care of Chuck for you
When you've got other things to do.'

4.42

The weekend kicks off with a glorious
Brunch at an open-air café.
Champagne and omelettes. Ed's censorious
Conscience is dormant for a day.
They drive across to Sausalito;
Later, divide a vile burrito
From Taco Hut, and wash it down
With a Dos Equis, cool and brown.
Ed suggests tennis next, and trounces
His friend with effortless panache;
To cool themselves they take a splash
In Schwarz's pool, where Phil denounces
Schwarz as the dullest, dimmest, and
Least soulful beast of sea or land.

4.43

The iguana stares: obtuse, phlegmatic,
Full five feet long from tail to snout,
He complements Ed's sharp, erratic
Essence (as wurst does sauerkraut).
With evening, Ed and Phil go walking
Through the calm city—laughing, talking;
A mentor's what Ed needs; and Phil,
Warm and Socratic, fits the bill.
At night, Ed brings in his iguana.
Phil eyes him warily, while he
Eyes Philip just as warily.
Phil tries to bribe him. A banana?
The monster bloats his jowls at this,
Emitting his hoarse gular hiss.

4.44

'Phil, don't annoy.' 'The causation
Should run from him to me instead . . .
But I suppose I'm on probation.
Where will he sleep?' 'Beneath our bed.'
'Beneath our *bed*? His least vibration
Will rock the room to its foundation.'
'Don't slander Schwarz.' 'Well, on your head
Be it if one of us is dead
By dawn—' 'It's just for the duration
That the heat's knocked out in his shed.
I'll fix it. If it's cold,' says Ed,
'And Schwarz goes into hibernation,
It could be months . . .' The quadruped
Advances now with torpid tread.

4.45

They sleep. (There is no other option.)
Their ectothermic chaperone,
Taking to his in-house adoption,
Sinks into slumber like a stone.
Ed goes next day to church, confession;
He strays home with a lost expression,
And mumbles, 'Phil . . . I don't know quite
If what we're doing is . . . is right.'
'What do you mean?' asks Philip, puzzled:
'We both—' 'I know,' says Ed at length,
'I've prayed to God to give us strength
To—Phil, I—O my God, I've muzzled
Love's only true voice, Jesus Christ,
Who came to earth and sacrificed

4.46

His life for me . . . for me, a sinner.'
Phil looks at Ed, then says, 'My friend,
Let's fix that heating. After dinner
We'll talk this out.' But dinner's end
Sees Ed in new heart altogether,
As if a cloudburst of black weather
Had been dispersed and, rinsed by storm,
The night is generous and warm.
Phil looks at this good-looking lover's
Face as he prays: its casque of peace
Cleansed of all turbulent caprice
And guilt, and, as they pull the covers
Over themselves, says, 'Ed, I'm glad
For these three evenings that we've had . . . '

4.47

What does Phil see in Ed? Why does he
Seem so committed to him? True,
Once at a party, drunk and fuzzy
—John would be shaken if he knew—
Phil made it with a guy at college.
(Well, once or twice.) And he'd acknowledge,
Even when married, now and then,
His eye might stray toward other men.
But that's it. And, though unconventional,
That too seems meager cause why he
Should fall for Ed so speedily.
Not that affection is intentional
Or that, in matters of the heart,
We should pull leaf and leaf apart . . .

4.48

But still: Phil's always been attracted
By vulnerable people; Ed,
Eager, confused, intent, abstracted,
Is passionate in both speech and bed.
How good it is to be admired;
And how much more to be desired!
Ed's restlessnesses, sudden calms,
And, as he lies in Philip's arms,
His sad and serious expression
Affect Phil more than he can say.
Thus, in a strange, contagious way,
Ed's very lack of self-possession
Reduces Phil's, and so destroys
The outer suburbs of his poise.

4.49

Next morning, at first light, Ed, waking,
Kneels down in silence on the floor.
A calm and chilly dawn is breaking
Over the bay. As his first chore,
He goes to nurture his iguana
With three persimmons, a sultana,
Some lettuce, and an unripe yam
(a favorite, with a dab of jam).
Now Phil awakens from his coma:
'Monday! I guess I'd better call
The Peaceniks, then head south for Paul.'
They drive down to the Café Soma
(On 12th and Howard, close to where
Ed works); and order breakfast there.

4.50

Over large cups of coffee, steaming
And fragrant, Ed says, 'Phil, last night
I almost thought that I was dreaming.
But now—I know it wasn't right.
I have to trust my faith's decisions,
Not batten on my own volitions.
The Bible says, if a man lie
With a man, he must surely die.
It's in Leviticus, chapter 20,
Verse 13—which means it's as true
For me, a Christian, as for you.'
Phil laughs: 'That old book, Ed, holds plenty
Of rules that may have made sense once
—Take shellfish—but you'd be a dunce

4.51

To trim your heart by its sharp letter.
That kills, as someone sometime said.
What's wrong with sex? The more the better
If you like someone.' Flushing red,
Ed frowns and says, 'Don't bring in shellfish.
That's trivial . . . How can I be selfish
And lust for flesh instead of truth?
It's like a kid with a sweet tooth
On a no-sugar diet breaking
Into a cookie store for me
To put myself where I can be . . .'
'Tempted?' prompts Phil: 'No point my taking
Exception to your version of
Who first suggested making love.'

4.52

'Phil—please—don't . . . how can I explain it?
The point is that my body is
Not mine alone—I don't disdain it—
But it's God's instrument—my bliss
Is in his will—and its perfection
Resides in love, whose chief projection
Is to give life. All other use
Falls shorts of this. It is abuse
Even if lovers feel they're loving
When our will fails, we've got to pray,
"Help thou my unbelief." That way . . .'
'That's bullshit. Ed, what are you proving?
That two men or two women don't . . .'
'Phil, try to understand.' 'I won't

4.53

I can't . . . (His voice shakes) . . . You were saying,
Before I interrupted, God
Will help our unbelief, our fraying
Resolve. But what was wrong or odd
With last night's loveliness between us?
Given a God, if he had seen us
And he is just and loving-kind,
Why should you think that he would mind
My touch, your trembling, our caresses,
The loving smart in your clear eyes,
My hands ruffling your hair, our sighs?
If anything, I'd say he blesses
The innocent bodies that express
So forthrightly such happiness.

4.54

That's how I feel. But for the lecture
And weekend, thank you, Ed.' His eyes
Meet Ed's, and with a sad conjecture
Ed asks, 'We'll keep in touch?' They rise.
'Sure, sure,' Phil mumbles. 'You can write me.'
Ed says, 'Phil, why don't you invite me
Down to your place sometime perhaps?'
'Yes, anytime, feel free . . .' They lapse
Into a bitter silence. Gilding
The great bole of a churchyard oak
The angled sun now shifts to soak
With liquid light Ed's office building,
Near which, with nothing more to say,
The two shake hands and turn away.

Six Inches

R. Raj Rao

5 a.m. The alarm rings. I switch it off and go back to sleep. Then I wake up and jump out of bed. It's one of those writing days again. I brush my teeth and switch on the electric kettle to prepare my morning tea. When the tea is ready, I sit on a chair opposite my bed and sip it.

5.30 a.m. I clear my desk and stare at the blank white sheets of paper before me. I have to turn them into a screenplay for a TV film. The money's good and it would mean a couple of months of hassle-free existence. I've been working the thing out in my head over the past few days. Now it's time to write. I pore over my notes.

1. Ext. Sahar Airport. Bombay. Night.
   (*Rashid clears customs, picks up his bags and baggage claim. Ashok spots him and waves out excitedly. Rashid comes out of Terminal Two, puts his bags on the ground and hugs Ashok. Then he kisses him. Ashok picks up one of the two suitcases. Rashid and Ashok walk towards the car, exchanging pleasantries. It's an old red Maruti that belongs to Rashid. Their arms are around each other's waists. They drive from the airport, using the Western Express Highway, to Rashid's flat at Seven Bungalows, Versova, Bombay, where they live. Ashok is at the wheel.*)
   Ashok: But you look well. The trip's done you good. I thought the month would never end.
   Rashid: Did you miss me? Hope you haven't been

naughty while I was gone.

Ashok: Of course I have. Tell me, how's New York?

Rashid: Wicked. As wicked as ever.

(*Jazz music on the car stereo. Although it's late, the roads are still full of peak-hour traffic. When they reach the apartment block, they park in the building's basement parking area and haul the bags to the elevator.*)

2. Int. Rashid's well-furnished flat. Night.

(*Rashid and Ashok are seated on a four-poster double bed, an imitation antique from Chor Bazaar. Rashid is unpacking his bags, his stuff spread all over the bed. The other furniture in the room, which includes a table and chair and wooden almirah, is similar to the bed. A framed black-and-white picture of a scene from the film* Possession du Condamne *hangs on the wall opposite the bed. Above the bed is a huge blow-up of Shah Rukh Khan. Rashid produces a cheque for $200 from his wallet and flashes it at Ashok.*)

Rashid: Sweety, I've brought you an unusual present. It's not big bucks by American standards, but that's not the point. It'll allow you to exploit your creative perversities to the fullest. *Six Inches*, that satanic men's magazine we both adore so much, wants us to send them five or six unpornographic action photographs of Indian men, as a sample. I met Richard Franklin, the editor, personally, told him what a great photographer you were and everything, showed him specimens of your work, and wrangled this advance. It works out to over thirty dollars per picture, don't you see? How many rupees is that?

Ashok: I'm not impressed, Meaty. It's hazardous work, although I'll be flattered to be published in *Six Inches*. People in India are no longer so naïve. If they suspect what we're up to, we've had it.

Rashid: But you'll do it all the same. For my sake. Won't you love? If our samples are okayed, there'll be more orders coming our way. At higher rates.

Ashok: Meaty, I don't know why you insist on thinking that photography is like your fashion designing stuff. First the samples are okayed, then orders follow.

3. Int. Robes, Rashid's retail outlet at Flora Fountain. Day.

(*Rashid swings open the plate glass doors, enters and greets his sales staff who are eagerly awaiting his arrival. Salesman 1 is taking the trouser measurements of a young man. Rashid goes over to him, snatches the measuring tape from his hands, and takes the young man's measurements himself. He allows his fingers to linger on the man's crotch for just that extra second. His measurements taken, the young man leaves.*)

Salesman 1: How was your trip, boss?

Rashid: Gorgeous!

Salesman 2: Any new designs and things?

Rashid: Many. But I haven't unpacked yet. They're still in my suitcases.

Salesman 3: Will you bring them tomorrow, boss? We're dying to have a look.

Rashid: Not tomorrow. I'm going to be away for another week. You guys will have to look after the place as brilliantly as you have been doing all these days. Sweety and I are on a major photography assignment. See you Monday next. Bye.

(*Rashid leaves the shop, starts his Maruti and drives off.*)

8.30 a.m. Three hours to write a mere three scenes. I'm that slow. I switch on the radio. I'm a Vividh Bharati freak. I get carried away by a song and stop writing.

9 a.m. I lower the volume of the radio but do not switch it off. I'm afraid of too much quiet.

4. Int. The flat. Night.

(*Rashid and Ashok lie in bed in nightsuits. They are having an argument about the impending assignment.*)

Rashid: You never, never stand by me. You're always letting me down.

Ashok: And you're always taking me for granted. You act as if you own me.

Rashid: I don't care about you. I want your work to be known on the international circuit.

Ashok: That's exactly it. I'm not good enough for you the way I am. It's yourself you care about, not me.

Rashid: Sweety, that's mean. You know it isn't true.

Ashok: You think I'm your slave.

Rashid: No.

Ashok: You keep me in your flat, allow me to drive your car, so you can control my will.

Rashid: No. No.

Ashok: Stop screaming or you'll bring the neighbours out.

Rashid: I'm not screaming. It's you.

Ashok: Stop.

(*Rashid is crying. Ashok switches off the lights.*)

5. Int. The flat. Day.

(*Rashid and Ashok have made up. They are in the little study with a bookshelf. On the walls are portraits of Oscar Wilde and scenes from* Death in Venice. *There is also a writing table and a chair. A map of Bombay is spread out on the floor before them. They are discussing the possible sites where they can shoot.*)

10 a.m. I put paperweights on all my loose sheets of paper. I have Kellogg's cornflakes and jam toast for breakfast and get back to my desk.

11 a.m. Most people in Bombay are in their offices at this time, but I'm jobless. I have no office. Sometimes I call myself a freelancer, but it's only a euphemism. I'm really a hack. In the age of political correctness in which we live, there's plenty of work for me. And for others like me: feminists, dalits, blacks. Maybe we should form a brotherhood.

6. Ext. Chowpatty Beach. Evening.

(*There are hundreds of men who have gathered on the sands for no apparent reason. Many of them hold hands, or have their arms around each other's shoulders and waists. Rashid and Ashok* camouflage themselves in the crowd. Ashok has a camera hanging from his neck. He searches for the appropriate shot, then zeroes in on a pair who clasp each other so low on the waist that they virtually look like they're clasping arse. The boys turn around and burst out laughing.)

Boy 1: Foreign tourist, sir?

Rashid: No love, we're Indian.

Boy 2: Want to posing with me, sir?

Rashid: Why not, love?

(Rashid poses with Boy 2 while Ashok clicks. They quickly bid goodbye to the boys and move away, but the boys keep looking at them curiously.)

7. Ext. The Marine Drive wall. Evening.

(*The wall is lined with people from Hotel Nataraj to the Air India building at Nariman Point. Rashid and Ashok walk as if on a march past, closely scanning the faces that are seated before them. They stop before two collegians, one of whom has his leg on his friend's. Ashok physically rearranges the lads in such a way that one's knee is almost on the other's crotch. He clicks.*)

Collegian 1: Are you guys press men or something?

Rashid: That's right. Press men. (*stressing the word*)

Ashok: We're doing a story on Marine Drive.

Rashid: You know, the different faces of Marine Drive.

Collegian 2: For which newspaper? Or is it a magazine?

Rashid: *Newsweek.* You've heard of *Newsweek*?

Collegian 2: Yes, make sure our pics are used, okay?

Rashid: Of course, love. Bye. See you soon.

12.30 p.m. This writing is a lonely business. I actually welcome it when the telephone rings. But there's only a screeching noise in the receiver when I pick it up.

I disconnect the phone. It doesn't ring again. I feel like masturbating. I just did it two hours ago, but I want to do it again.

1 p.m. I go to the balcony and see office-goers at lunch, patronizing the vendors on the street.

8. Int. The flat. Night.

(*Rashid and Ashok are sitting in the drawing room. It's full of cane furniture—sofa set, side tables, dining table, chairs. On the walls are original paintings by Raza, Gieve Patel, Jehangir Sabavala. A half-full bottle of Royal Challenge lies on the teapoy, along with platefuls of munchies. Both Rashid and Ashok hold their glasses in their hands and drink.*)

Rashid: Sweety, I'm sorry for what happened the other night. You're such a darling. What interesting pictures we clicked this evening.

Ashok: Me too, Meaty. And to tell you the truth, I'm enjoying it more than I imagined.

(*They drink for a while. Then they make love.*)

9. Int. Churchgate Station. Day.

(*Rashid and Ashok wade through the crowd to reach Platform Four, where a train is pulling in. They select a second class compartment and shoot. The compartment is so overpacked that the commuters, as they alight, virtually look as if they are on top of one another, especially as Ashok takes the picture from floor level.*)

10. Int. The flat. Night.

(*Rashid and Ashok are in bed in their nightsuits. They are drunk. Rashid is crying.*)

Rashid: You're a cheat. A voyeur. That's why you want to take so many notorious pictures. You're getting a vicarious thrill out of it.

Ashok: Meaty, don't get me started again. You're the one who . . . forget it. Go back to sleep, will you? We've got to be out shooting early in the morning.

Rashid: I'm going to smash your camera on the Marine Drive wall. It's your cunning alibi.

Ashok: Shut up. Or you'll have your head smashed.

Rashid: Liar. Voyeur. I know what you were up to in my flat when I was away in the US. You're not even queer. You pose as one because it's trendy.

Ashok: Meaty, we've been through this before. Just cut it out. I'm tired and want to crash.

(*Rashid continues to cry. Ashok switches off the lights.*)

11. Ext. The Bombay streets. Morning.

(*Rashid and Ashok are driving from Versova into town. Both have a hangover. As he is driving past Mahim creek, Ashok notices two men squatting, facing each other as they excrete. He stops the car, steps out and walks towards them. Rashid doesn't know what's going on. Before the squatting men are aware of it, Ashok photographs them, runs back to the car and speeds off. Rashid is amazed at his courage.*)

Rashid: Sweety, that was neat.

Ashok: Did anyone see us?

Rashid: No, but I saw one of the two men zipping up and coming at us yelling.

Ashok: You're joking.

Rashid: I'm not. I swear.

(*Jazz music in the car. As they drive they look for suitable shots. They do not find any.*)

3 p.m. I drive away the crow on the window sill. Its incessant cawing ruins my concentration. And I don't need any visitors. I light up, first one cigarette, then another. I dream of my script being accepted. Then I fear its rejection. On the grounds of obscenity. After all, we live in an age of high fundamentalism.

12. Int. The Talk of the Town restaurant at Marine Drive. Day.

(*Rashid and Ashok park their car outside the restaurant, enter and occupy a vacant table. They order coffee. Rashid ogles at the waiters. Ashok looks at them through the lens of his camera.*)

13. Int. Robes. Day.

(*Rashid and Ashok are in an air-conditioned cabin at the far end of the shop. This is Rashid's office. Salesman 1 brings him some vouchers which he goes through and signs. Ashok is smoking. Rashid gives instructions to his salesmen.)*

4 p.m. I switch on the kettle and make myself a cup of tea. The neighbour's children are playing outside my front door and tap on it frequently. My neighbours think I'm a saint.

6 p.m. I've just woken up after a siesta. I never intended to take a nap so I wonder how it happened.

14. Int. The flat. Night.

(Rashid and Ashok are in the drawing room listening to music. Each has a glass in his hand.)

Ashok: I think the pictures are going to be wonderful.

Rashid: I bet they are. Big bucks in the offing and all because of me.

Ashok: There's bigger money in porn. The next time you're in the US, get me an assignment that requires me to photograph Arab men doing it.

Rashid: Voyeur.

15. Ext. Janmashtami. Day.

(A group of young men in shorts has just arrived with a lot of fanfare [music, drums etc]. They form a pyramid and attempt to break the pot of curd that is tied between two five-storied buildings. People throw buckets of water on them from the balconies of the buildings. Rashid and Ashok who are in the car, get out and stand with the cheering crowds. Ashok takes out his camera and clicks several times. His prize shot is when the men lose their balance, just as they've made it, and tumble over each other's heads, their wet shorts prominent.)

Rashid *(sighing)*: God, imagine the state of their balls.

Ashok: Not to worry. They know how to protect their vital organs.

(They continue to stand and watch until the group succeeds in breaking the dahi handi amidst a lot of din. Then they disperse along with the crowds and get into their car.)

16. Ext. An open-air gym at VT: opposite the Capitol Cinema. Evening.

(*Several youngsters dressed only in shorts are exercising with a variety of instruments. Their bodies glisten with perspiration. Rashid and Ashok who have obtained the permission of the man in charge, take close-ups of the more good-looking men, busy with their dumb-bells. The men are amused. Some of them comb their hair.*)

17. Int. The flat. Night.

(*Rashid and Ashok are smoking in the balcony.*)

Ashok: Meaty, I'm learning so much about the intricacies of my craft. How a photograph can so completely distort the meaning of an action if it pleases. I'm indebted to you for the insight.

Rashid: For once you're giving me credit. Thank you Richard Franklin, editor of *Six Inches*. Thank you all our models.

(*They kiss.*)

7 p.m. I fill my fountain pen. I want to drink the poisonous substance.

18. Ext. A nondescript street. Day.

(*Rashid and Ashok are walking behind two well-built men in their late twenties. From time to time the men stop and one of them lifts the other ecstatically. They are evidently very happy about something. Every time they stop, Rashid and Ashok stop too, maintaining a safe distance of about twenty feet. Every time they embrace, Ashok goes slightly closer and takes a picture. He has just taken his fourth shot, when the men suddenly turn around. The joyous expression on their faces have gone. It is replaced by a stern, suspicious look. The conversation that follows takes place in Hindi.*)

Man 1: Hey mister, what is it? Why did you click our pictures?

Ashok: No reason in particular. I'm a photographer by

training and I just click whatever catches my fancy. Sorry if you feel bad.

Man 2: But why us? What did you find so special about us?

Rashid: The friendship between the two of you. In these days of strife and hatred it's so reassuring.

Man 1: Where do you two work?

Rashid: I'm a businessman. Ashok is a photographer, as he's already told you.

Man 2 (*to Rashid*): What business do you do?

Rashid: Textile business.

Man 2: Why do you speak like a *chhakka*?

Rashid: What do you mean? It's my natural style.

Man 1 (*to Ashok*): Can I take a look at your camera?

Ashok: Sure. Why not?

(*He gives his camera to Man 2 who scrutinizes and then returns it.*)

Man 2: Is your camera imported?

Ashok: No, it's Indian.

Man 1: Is it very expensive?

Ashok: No, not much. Less than a thousand rupees.

Man 2: Will you show us our pictures when they're developed?

Ashok: Of course. Tell us where we can contact you.

Man 2: Why don't you give us your address or telephone number?

Rashid (*to Ashok, in English*): No, Sweety, don't do that. It's risky.

Man 2 (*to Rashid*): Hey mister, we understand English, okay?

Ashok (*to Man 2*): We are in the process of moving house. So you give us your address, and we'll see that the pictures reach you.

Man 2: I'm at the BDD Chawls at Worli, room number 22.

Ashok: Okay, I'll see you there with the photos.

Man 1: One moment. Do the two of you live together?

Ashok: Yes, we're flatmates. We must leave now. We've got to attend a meeting.

(*Before the men can say anything else, they quickly get into their car and drive off.*)

19. Ext. The Bombay streets. Day.

(*Rashid and Ashok are driving.*)

Ashok: Meaty, I told you this would happen. Those chaps were cops.

Rashid: They were thieves. They wanted to steal your camera.

Ashok: That's just lower middle class mentality. Don't tell me you're not used to it, having lived all your life in Bombay.

Rashid: And they were rogues. They wanted our address so they could come and blackmail us.

Ashok: I know that. But why did you have to tell me in front of them? It made them all the more suspicious. I was much more tactful. I told them we were moving house.

Rashid: Fuck them. Are you serious about going to their place with the snaps? You must be mad if you are.

8 p.m. I don't know why, but I feel terribly depressed all of a sudden. I pace the room for a while.

20. Int. The Liberty Studio at Fort. Day.

(*Rashid and Ashok are giving in their film for developing. They are asked by the manager to collect the pictures two days later. They come out of the studio and get into their car. After they drive off, we see the two men on the opposite side of the street. They have followed Rashid and Ashok and are tracking their movements. They enter the studio and have a word with the manager.*)

21. Int. The flat. Night.

(*Rashid and Ashok enter. They have had a drink on the way.*)

Rashid: Fishy odour. You're smelling of spunk, naughty boy.

Ashok: It's the Versova seashore. What else can you expect when you live in a fishing village?

Rashid: I want to eat fish and chips. And I want to sing a song called 'Penis in Your Anus'.

8.30 p.m. I pour myself a drink. Maybe that'll do me, though not my liver, some good. The doorbell rings, but there's no one there. Those neighbours' kids . . .

9 p.m. Tomorrow I'll take out the typewriter and type out what I'm writing today. I am a one-finger typist. I don't understand word-processors or anything too technologically advanced. It's a sort of impotence.

22. Int. The Liberty Studio at Fort. Evening.

(*Rashid and Ashok are collecting their photographs. To their surprise, they find the two men in the studio, waiting for them. Even more surprising, the photographs are already in their possession. Seeing this, Rashid loses his head and screams at the manager.*)

Rashid: How dare you give our snaps to these fellows.

Man 2 (*flashing an identity card*): Police!

Ashok (*to Rashid*): I told you.

(*The rest of the conversation is in Hindi.*)

Ashok (*to the policemen*): But how did you know we gave our rolls for developing here?

Man 1: We followed you on a motorcycle after our infamous encounter the other day. We waited till you left the shop and then told the manager who we were and what we wanted.

Ashok: But I thought we had parted as friends on the understanding that we'd bring you your snaps at BDD Chawls.

Man 2: That was according to you, not according to us. (*He produces the photographs and we see each one of them at close quarters. They look sinister.*) We demand an explanation. Why have you taken all these photographs? What do you intend to do with them?

Man 1: The pictures look dirty. Your intentions are malafide.

Man 2 (*to Ashok*): Is your friend a foreigner?

Ashok: No, he's Indian.

Man 2: Which part of India is he from?

Ashok: He's Parsi.

Man 2: Bawaji?

Man 1: You'll have to come with us to the police station.

Rashid: What for?

Man 1: For taking these pictures.

Rashid: Why make such a hullabaloo about them? They are merely Bombay shots that depict different aspects of life in the city.

Man 1: We're not convinced. You'll have to come to the police station.

Rashid: What nonsense!

Man 2: Hey, mind your language. Don't use words like 'nonsense' or you'll get it.

Ashok (*to the men*): Look yaar. Can't we settle this amicably?

Man 1: What do you mean? Are you trying to bribe us?

10 p.m. The drink has done my spirits some good. I feel less depressed. I pace the room again.

23. Int. The flat. Early morning.

(*The double bed in the bedroom has been separated into two single beds. Light filters in through the curtains.*

Rashid and Man 2 are asleep on one bed. Ashok and Man 1 on the other. They are covered in blankets. Ashok wakes up, sits up in bed and surveys the situation. There's an action-replay of events going on in his head.)

Cut to: Flashback of events that transpired the previous evening, sequentially.

24. Ext. Liberty Studio. Evening.

(*The two policemen strike a deal with Rashid and Ashok*

outside the studio. Currency notes are exchanged and the four are seen getting into Rashid's car. Ashok as usual is at the wheel.)

25. Int. Gokul Restaurant and Bar at Colaba, Saturday night.
(Rashid, Ashok and the two policemen have downed several drinks and are in the process of ordering dinner. The other tables are full of gay couples who are drunk and all over each other. It's a totally new experience for the policemen who are enjoying themselves thoroughly.)

26. Ext. The Bombay streets. Night.
(Rashid, Ashok and the two policemen, all very drunk, drive from Colaba to Versova. On the way they stop briefly at the BDD chawls. They sing incoherent songs and have close shaves on the road, even at this late hour.)

27. Int. The flat. Early morning.
(Ashok wonders whether he and Rashid seduced the policemen or the policemen seduced them. He goes back to sleep. We hear all of them snoring.)

(Credits)

Midnight. I gobble up a lot of stale food which has been lying in the fridge for days. It is quiet now. The neighbours' kids are fast asleep. I'm frightened of too much quiet.

Karate

Adil Jussawalla

Eyes sewn, my head a bag of tricks,
I pad down streets to find my enemy.

New York London or any tall
Story I've a part in,
He is the same

White man whose daily dis-
Appearance is my brief.
Whose wars have put me on a false, if nimble
Footing. Whose tame goings-on
By day
Conceal a fratricidal fox by night.

What is it
Disproportions me of my big-time twin,
Symbiosis of loving that must kill? What pigmy
In me wants it?

I spot a giant. Call
So he won't disappear down the fatal
Error of some steps. Warn him
As he comes:

Before night

Takes in its tongue with its yellow pill,
Before day
Swallows it with a smile,
Before dawn
Breaks round his head the lights of his last
Aromatic breath,

His head will flop,
My hands will chop, then fold.

The Raising of Lazarus

for Adrian Husain

Adil Jussawalla

The rapid indirections of a trip,
A hand of stone secure about the throat,
God's hateful hiss of air as through a tin . . .
Reversal of a process I had been through
Snaking back to sleep.
Until I felt his mouth's coherence lift,
I had forgotten what it was to die.

And then remembered: the slow
Brutalities his knowledge drew to scorn—
Scorn of my condition, scorn
Of scorn itself, scorn of my last petering
Outwards from his hands.
He brought me round but never asked the matter
With my life nor why it went.
Nor took the fatal tablets from my coat.

Song of a Hired Man

Adil Jussawalla

I'm head of this affair,
    rioter, home-made
    red-flagging bum;
singing of hope for a fee
though nobody wants it—No.
Have aged to the shape of a crow,
    saying Ave's for Bhave
    selling undies to rundies.
Cheat everyone,
No one cheats me.

Sleep at odd
angles and hours
since she went at a crossroads
of sunstroke, killed for no ice.
    Bark. Anger the run-down
at their siesta—their open-jawed
    fledglings awaiting my worms,
    my children, my followers;
    myself, a snatcher
    of eggs, stray cats,
    upstart crow who flaps
big-bottomed foreign-returneds
    who pay court
    (tennis of course)

to their Laxmis, their banks,
their dicks perpetually depressed.

Stars that gave out
    at the burial of sailors at sea,
    swam through her eyes,
    now the eyes of girls who stare
as I pass
    (if I had the wings of a dove
    I could dove-tail so sweetly)
till a steel-genitalled Jaguar stops me,
Miss (mortified) India at the wheel.
    But I make do somehow,
    tickling the teat of a temple—
    learnt evasive action
    from a colonel, British,
    my love-life easy.

Hot tropical trains
aprickle with limbs and eyes,
    ribbed nags
under a masjid's shadow,
    the hack's long
agony, engineer whips and wheels
are not my concern.
I'm head of affairs far sweeter,
    more bitter—Love's soft
    partition alone responsible, O
    for scars
    on the neck,
    on the back,
    on the throat—
    proud flesh, bound
for the skeleton-scraper.

Followers of all
    the pallidly orthodox
I shunned, all unfelt needles.
A beach lies before me
    asprawling with boats,
    the cotton-city emptying
    its spindle of people
into the sea—along with
this elephant god I carry
    asquat on a rat.
    Hai Ram!
the fine oppositions of the Hindu
    imagination—
as lean as fire
as fat as fat.

Slap-happy,
    dissolve now,
    dissolve, bright clay,
    and from my possession,
work deep in the sea, dissolve,
    waste deep . . .
    and perhaps . . .
    after another ten years
    of this ritual
    dunking, debunking . . .

after ten years, what?

Alone by the sea now,
    count my gains.
Singing of hope means
a little less pain,
a little more change—
    that seems to be all.

Got your Black Label quota.
Got the Godfather's call.
I'm head of this affair,
 rioter, home-made, let.

'Never Take Candy from a Stranger!'

Gyansingh Shatir

Dear readers! I am like a wild plant which is reared by the elements but whoever happens to see its flowers, starts plucking them and destroying them. There is a saying in the village:

> God must not bless anyone with fair colour,
> It is like inviting the enmity of the whole town.

In view of this saying, my fair colour was enough to make me a victim of circumstances but my ill-luck was such that my features were charming too. Whoever happened to look at me liked me and started kissing and fondling me. Some would embrace me with their looks. To escape their amorous glances, I would cast down my eyes and go away from their presence. If I did not move away from their gaze, I felt the onlooker was tearing through me as if eating me. None of the other children could match up to my good looks. I would look at myself in the mirror, store my picture in my eyes and compare myself with others. Everybody seemed to me a combination of unrelated limbs; creativity's half-hearted attempts. Whoever appealed to me a little, I would look at him with the eyes of a critic. Some had crooked eyebrows, some unequal eyes, some had mismatching nostrils and uneven lips. The ears never seemed to match the faces.

Yet, I noticed that my face was as if a painter had drawn

a centre line before painting the organs on it. My countenance made me a self-worshipper. When I looked in the mirror, I wished to love myself and started kissing the mirror. This new experience transported me to a new extravagance of jealousy. I touched myself, kissed myself and with a desire to embrace my rival, I would look behind the mirror and finding no one there I would feel aggrieved. I was very fond of the mirror and always kept a broken piece of it in my pocket. But I lost that precious possession somewhere and could not manage to find another after that. To get rid of my agony, I invented a new game. I went to graze the cattle and sat down by the stream at such an angle that I could see myself in the water. This side of the Satrukha, there was a hunched rosewood tree, whose branches had spread over the water like a cape. The branches stood at a good height above the water and it was my favourite place. I sat there for hours and watched myself in the water-mirror like the lotus of the legends. It is said that the lotus was actually an angel. He happened to see his face in the water once and it delighted him so much that he forgot his divine duty. He was banished from the kingdom of God with a curse that he would forever stand in water but would never be able to see his own charming face.

The girls admired me and would offer anything to enjoy my company. They cajoled and caressed me and took me away with them. It was difficult for me to choose between Parkash Kaur and Swarn Kaur. They would decide my fate by a toss and whoever won would press me close to her bosom and sleep as if there were thieves around conspiring to steal me from her.

Kirpal Kaur was the same age as I was. She was crazy about me and never played with anybody else. She roamed about aimlessly when she was alone. She would hold my hands like a mirror before her eyes, kiss them and rub them on her body. I would enquire why she did that. She would say: 'I may steal some of your colour this way.' When she tried to make me kiss her, I refused, fearing that her black colour would rub off on me. She did everything to see her desire fulfilled. She brought roasted grain, pulses, sugar candy and sugarcane from her field for me. When she could not manage anything, she got me flowers. She would decorate my hair with those flowers and proclaim: 'You are my Krishna and I am your Radha.'

Once she saw me pissing and it was as if she had found something unique. She came closer and looked inquisitively. She was astonished and immediately tried to imitate my style. But she could not piss beyond her feet and wet them. It was a strange discovery for me. I was proud of myself and she was ashamed. I put a precondition for playing with her, 'You must piss as far as I do, only then will I play with you.'

My unyielding attitude confused her. She tried to please me in divergent ways. She would push her loins forward, throw her head back and piss with all the force she could muster. Her colour grew deep crimson in her efforts but she could not manage to piss beyond her feet. When she could not compete in the game, she grew dispirited and asked, 'Why don't I have the thing you have?'

'Only a boy will have such a thing, you are no boy,' I would catch hold of my organ and tell her with pride.

Once I knew her weakness, I started impressing her in many ways. I turned round while pissing, made the urine flow in an arc or a circle, as I wished. I held my organ facing upward so that the flow rose toward the sky and then dropped down. Kirpal Kaur witnessed this scene and applauded spontaneously. She would hold my organ in one hand, caress her groin and at last withdraw dejectedly. But she seldom remained in that mood. She grew hopeful the next moment and persuaded me to rub my organ on her groin. When I asked why, she replied, 'Something like that may sprout here in due course of time.' She would lie underneath me, even though my weight prevented her from breathing smoothly and held me over her. She was happy to see me naked. Even if I did not fulfil her desire to her satisfaction, she would say, 'I like your nakedness. I wish I could see you like this forever.'

Then it so happened that Lashkar Singh came from Sargodha with a little cart powered by a hand-crank. The cart became so popular with the children that they could not stop talking about it. When he took out the cart from his outhouse, the children stopped playing, encircled him and begged him to give them a joyride. He refused to oblige everyone but when I asked he would accede to my demand readily.

One morning I was returning from the fields, when I saw Lashkar had just closed the door of his outhouse and was about to bolt it. When he saw me he stopped abruptly and asked lovingly, 'Want a ride?'

What was there to ask! Riding the go-cart was like riding a flying chariot. I ran impulsively, pushed the door open and barged in. My impulse was so sudden that if Lashkar Singh had not left the bolt at the right time, he would have fallen in. The go-cart was kept in the veranda and I ran to sit on it. It was my first chance to have that sweet go-cart all to myself. I had always wanted to have a close look at it, ride it to my heart's content, but never had a chance because of the crowd. I went up to the go-cart and started caressing its body and appreciating its design. It had everything that a loaded motorcar should have. On the driver's seat was a wooden mannequin dressed as a chauffeur and on the other seats black corks were placed, which looked like passengers against the white painted background. Between the two rows of seats there was a line of red paint which looked like a carpet. The roof was made of bright tin, which resembled a steel mirror. I made faces at the mirror. It was fascinating. From different angles, I could see my face change. Just then Lashkar Singh came from behind and kissed my cheeks noisily. I did not like it. I cleaned the spit off my cheek and looked at him angrily. He said affectionately, 'Do you like the go-cart?'

'Yes, I love it.' My anger abated and I replied, 'Let me

ride the go-cart to my heart's content,' spreading my arms as wide as I could.

He brought the go-cart outside the veranda, turned it towards the door, made me sit on it, cranked it and let go. It went at full speed and when it stopped, I felt the happiness in my bones. I was turning the go-cart back when Lashkar Singh came running to me and again cranked it; the go-cart hurtled down a slope and took me farther than before. By the time he reached me, I had already turned the car uphill and was sitting on it. He stood smiling before me, twirling the crank in his hand. I asked him to crank the go-cart. He bent over me and said luringly, 'I'll give you this cart but there is a condition.'

'What is that?'

I was so overjoyed that I could hear my own heart thumping.

'Give me five kisses.'

He showed me a five, spreading his fingers.

I was at the end of my patience and offered him my cheek. It was so spontaneous that there was no gap between his asking and my response. Kissing me, the threw me onto the ground. In my ecstasy I felt that he was loving and gave myself up to him.

Readers! Childhood is such a mirror of inexperience and simplicity of feelings that it does not recognize any blemish of the lover. I felt a piercing pain in my buttocks and felt as if I was tearing at the seam. I let out a full-throated cry which rent the air. Frightened, he let go of me and stood a little away from me. I stood up weeping and made towards the gate. He stopped me in my tracks and renewed his promise. As he came close to me, I drew back in fear, as if he were a monster. Had my cries not been frightening, he would not have opened the door for me. I was eager to complain about him and was weeping inconsolably. But when I went away from him, a strange fear came over me and I became calm. By the time I reached home I was feeling ill. I supported myself against a dark corner and then abruptly drew away from it, thinking that anything I touched would hurt me.

That delicate age! That repulsive incident! That self-restraint!

That unnatural sexual experience stuck to me like a shield which defended me from homosexuals in later life.

Will anybody believe the reality of my sentiments? After revealing this secret, I have gone through the same spiritual pain which the bloodthirst of that moment had made me feel. The memory of that incident still bites me like a poisonous snake. At that time my face was angelic and its beauty was that of the simple hill-folk. My countenance conveyed such softness and innocence that even a hungry carnivore would have spared me and licked me fondly. But a man's lust is that repugnant thing which in its frenzy of expression can shame the most frightful of imaginings. In the years after that experience, circumstances have made me inculcate tolerance but I cannot accept its fiendishness in any way.

The result of that event was that I stopped taking gifts from anybody. If a boy elder to me wished to see me alone I would run away from him. I would not accept gifts even from my dear friends.

Translated from the Urdu by the author and Hoshang Merchant

from Sheltered Flame

Iqbal Mateen

The following are extracts of some of the key episodes in the novel.

'I am yours now,' Kaushalia exclaimed. Dearbald jumped from his chair. He bent down towards Kaushalia, and she surrendered her lips to his. Pyare Lal kept smiling. His eyes kept coming back to Shanuja, lying asleep in the bed . . .

Kaushalia reached her room and started pounding the door noisily. She threw herself at it as it was bolted from inside. Somehow, the bolt slipped down, and the door flew open. Kaushalia almost fell to the floor inside the room.

Shanuja's shorts lay on the floor, and he was lying in Pyare Lal's bed, moaning. Kaushalia's eyes filled with terror . . .

Samsamuddin confided to Kaushalia: 'The forty-year-old son of the chief of the rich Pathan clan now keeps Shanuja. The boy wears women's clothes, puts on saris, has bangles round his wrists, applies lipstick to his lips, and . . . and, has two small bulges on his chest to look like breasts.' . . .

Hansen used to spice his account of Shanuja's new ways. He said that Shanuja was doing things which were not at all proper for boys. He said that Shanuja would augment his mother Kaushalia's income. 'Things which are done surreptitiously today will be done openly tomorrow. After all, now is the time when the "boy" can make money, and he is so ravishing. Kaushalia knows everything. Some rich fellow is "keeping" Shanuja, and she must have got a good price for the boy . . . She wanted a girl who, on growing up, would continue in the profession. Since she has a son, she has put him on the same track.' . . .

Kaushalia woke up and realized that Dearbald was not there.

'Dear, dear,' she called out.

She rose from her seat in a flash, lifted the mosquito curtain, and found that the bed had not been slept in. She turned around as if struck by lightning. The reality was revealed to her.

Someone was whispering into her ear: 'Shanuja has taken away your last solace. Are you Shanuja's mother, or a rival?'

No. No. No.

Like one gone mad she moved from room to room, until she reached Shanuja's room and started pounding the door furiously. Shanuja rose from the bed:

'Who is there?' he asked, in an irritated voice.

Someone was pounding the door like a mad person. Shanuja tried to cover his nude body with a shawl. Flower petals sticking to his back and buttocks fell to the floor. He wrapped the shawl round his body, reached the door and unbolted it. The two shutters flew open like a harlot's pleasure-chamber. Kaushalia asked him, 'Where is he?' Shanuja smiled. Without paying any heed to Kaushalia he said, 'I am not wearing any clothes. Under the shawl I am totally nude. Surprisingly, you are wearing clothes as though you never removed them during the night! It doesn't matter. But what surprises me is that even now you have not come to tell me that you are not my mother.'

Kaushalia felt the barb aimed at her. 'Shut up! Tell me where he is.'

'He has gone! And even if he had been here what could you have done to him?'

'So you have slept with him also! Do you know that he is . . .?'

Shanuja started. He realized that Kaushalia was referring not to Pyare Lal but to Dearbald.

Shanuja looked contemptuously at Kaushalia. 'He doesn't have the money to pay for my services.'

'Otherwise you would have become his?'

'No, no . . . I would have fallen at his feet and called him father. That's what you wanted, didn't you?'

Translated from the Urdu by Taqi Ali Mirza

from Yayati

Vishnu Khandekar

Devayani had flared up due to the developments of the last couple of hours. In a rage, she walked up to Puru and said to him, 'You are Puru, aren't you? Sharmishta's son? Then why are you keeping quiet now? She loved your father passionately, they say! You are the son of that same mother. You too must be doting on your father. What are you thinking about? Give your youth to your father! And take his old age instead!'

All the desires in my mind started shouting in my ears. 'That beautiful young woman is waiting for you in the salon. For the last fifteen days you have been waiting for her! Today when that glass of nectar is within your reach will you throw it away without drinking? Then what was the point of refusing to be an ascetic eighteen years ago? Think about it, you fool! Luckily you have been granted an antidote to the curse. Make use of it. What great harm would it do to Puru to accept your old age for a few years? On the other hand, he will get this kingdom in return. Get enjoyment for a few years; quench all your desires and then give Puru his youth back.'

Perhaps provoked by Devayani, Puru quickly came forward. He laid his head on my feet and said, 'Father, I am the son of that mother who, although being a princess, chose to be a slave for the sake of your lineage. I am prepared to take your old age.' 'All right' were the only two words that I uttered. Instantly realizing the implication of these words,

I closed my eyes. After a few moments I opened them to give my blessings to Puru, but I could not lift my hand. Puru was now standing in front of me as a very old man!

Devayani was astounded to see this miracle. She quickly left the palace along with Yadu.

Puru went and stood in front of a mirror. He took a good look at his appearance. For a moment he covered his face with both his hands. I could not make out whether he was regretting his sacrifice. But soon he was seated on the throne with a composed face. Looking at him I calmed down to some extent.

Earlier I had not been able to bear the sight of my own reflection. Now I could not bear the sight of Puru. Before leaving the town Sharmishta had sent a message for me: 'Let Puru always be blessed by the King.' Instead, today I had struck him with a thunderbolt. I felt like going near him, embracing him, consoling him, but only for a moment. I could not dare to do it. Sin is such a coward!

Translated by Nilesh Jahagirdar from the Marathi

Desire Brings Sorrow

for Eunice de Souza

Dinyar Godrej

Cool, no colour,
flawless shell
without even the stench
of your sea
You say
desire brings sorrow
and have done away
with it, pitched
your maw upon
a distant star
and now enjoy
gutless ananda.

It is not
an easy question of preferences
for us unlike you,
not the choice
of sweet over bitter,
but a concession
that love and lust
though terribly troublesome
are certainly not
without flavour.

Under Water

Dinyar Godrej

1.
Where are the quiet pools, flat and untroubled,
that mirror nothing?
Where are the depths, covered and shaded,
the wet beds of moss?

I have turned around a question
                    o my lover
till I have become a question
and memory is the noise of the sea
the crash of a wave that breaks upon me.

2.
A little creeping grief
grubbing the ocean floor

heart blot of
grim regularity
searching . . .

little clawing crust
working under pressure
the moss—long settled—swirls

3.
The land is alive with rain.

Children playing on the bank
have plunged a volley of stones
into our dull waters.

Forgotten coral uncovered
beauteous blood bloom,
the rising rush bubbles
with distant chords,
wrenched voices that reverberate.

See infant evil's rippling strength,
terror once dropped concentric grows.
The death ship passes, its bristling wake
glistening like a row of pearls.

4.
'I step out pure from my bath,' she said
'It's like a new birth.'
What was it she lost in there
that made her shine reappear?
I had to find out.

I slipped into the bath and it opened beneath me
I sank through the years to the ocean's bed
and looking up I could see no light
save the mockery of a luminous fish.

I tried speaking but my words were bubbles.
I could not rise for the world was over me.
Then I tried to give up trying
and suddenly the waters cleared.
I saw the continents moving

the world I had loved
afloat.

5.
The waters bore down the sacrifice
an old man, ashen and dead.
I am sure he did not feel
the scallops kiss
or the lick of currents—
those were beyond his knowing.
He was sent this way for a purpose.
Who knows whether it was fulfilled?
Several beings fed.

6.
Feel
        the pull
Atlantis was childhood sinking
a precious bubble
        the tug
the wreck weighted with bullion
was younglove
            the persistence
the poet's surrounded isles
were humanity
            of memory.

7.
The stone I dropped in the pool as a child,
its ripples now overwhelm me.

Walk carefully through these waters
                    my lover
for you are now within me.

It is the small fish that have taught me
the wisdom of fright.

On the Road to Jata Shankar

Dinyar Godrej

Through looming rocks the sky a jagged knife,
Underneath, trees crawled numerous millipede legs,
Between, the dirt road dipped out of sight too soon.
My mother fluttered birdlike,
Trapped in the plummeting cage of the car.
Her arms turned jelly and cold,
Her scant hair wet with sweat.
Passing swaying trees and outsized rocks
She could not bear to look, and said,
'Stop the car. I want to get out.
I'm feeling very frightened.' My father,
Unsettled by her shrill despair, hotly said,
'Don't be crazy! This road is quite travelled.
You can't get out here.'
                    But we did.
Mum and I walked to make the trees stop.
The shapeful rocks bought comments,
Flecked oddly as they were with pastel blue,
'Mum,' I said, 'You've been here before.
You weren't frightened then.' I can't
Explain my fear,' she said and wished
She had worn her walking shoes.
                    The rustle of dead leaves
Caused by some small scurrying turned

Attention to the overlordship of silence and
The magnitude of the dwarfing rocks,
Each frozen tree grappling roots in subterranean
                              battle,
Heaving stiffly under the impermanent road.
My mother couldn't bear how the sky narrowed
Miserably like some concept or
How the dark, deceptive road seemed so
Untravelled, not stretching cleanly as conscious
                              purpose,
But going oppressively, oppressedly winding on
Like a trick of the mind she thought
She'd overgrown or just forgotten.
Something happened. Did the sky turn blood red
And the leaves crawl over her skin?
The road, perhaps, shook like an old train,
The silence filled her mind with the hollowness of
                              bone?

When she reached the car parked in the shade
She grew calmer, remarking that it was lucky
There had been space to turn it around.

Apparently

Dinyar Godrej

Black dreams perch
upon seven o'clock.

They're lost in the shower.

Mouth open before the mirror
teeth, liquids, lumpen flesh—

What's the point/I am bad.
This gut simplicity
tears through my ears.

Simple the past.
Motherfather bore no knife,
the furniture was accepting.

This to a friend—
There is no reason for wanting to die.

Apparently
there doesn't have to be.

Rite of Passage

Manoj Nair

There are certain objects in this world that cannot be captured by the camera. Fireflies, for instance. Film-makers over the years have used artificial means to show them flitting across the screen. So every time you see them you are actually watching a few children holding candle flames and hopping across from one marked area to another as directed by the man in the chair.

Reminiscences, a few of them, are like those fireflies. They cannot be imprinted on the retina of the mind's eye. As a chief geologist at the National Geographical Society in Deogarh he has searched hard for prints of those college days. His first days.

They are for Prem like the moneyplant in his flat which has grown and crept into his drawing room. Every morning he watches the leaves flutter. He observes the emergence of a new one, pale green, greeting him saying: 'I'll be your guest for a few days.' Weekends are for sweeping out the fallen ones. Adieu, Adieu. Not a twist does he ever give the stem, so that it grows back out of the window to where it belongs.

Souvenirs from his college at Trissur. All arranged and set in place by his mother. Mother, who had brought him up since his father died. He was barely seven then. She was the one he listened to, and went to with his needs. If anyone questioned the reasoning behind his actions he would promptly reply: 'My mother told me to do so.' He can recollect all that with little embarrassment. His only reason to support a nationalist party's call to replace a historical mosque with a temple was the argument which always came veiled in another question: 'Who told you that the man you know as your father is your father?—Your mother of course.'

Often, her education was never the reason behind her advice. The lack of it was in fact the argument in favour. In natural bondings, faith is blind. Reasoning is illogical. Logic is unreasonable. Mother to son. Usha to Prem.

Going to college was literally climbing a hill to reach the seat of learning. But any thought of the three years he spent there were like the leaves of the moneyplant. They were not just his. They also belonged to Ramettan. Memory was not his right alone.

'Do you live close by?' was the first question Ramettan had asked when Prem went to him to collect his identity card.

'Yes,' he replied in a voice reciprocating the soft tone of the man behind the long wooden counter.

Ramettan was a popular man in college. Tall, swarthy, with a square face that held a prominent toothbrush moustache above a round drooping pair of shoulders, Ramettan was the only clerk in the office who would be at the service of any student wishing to check an attendance register, fill in the scholarship form, pay fees late but without fine . . .

'You can come to me any time you have a problem. I live on the college campus,' Ramettan had continued in the same vein. The softness stuck to him like glue spilling from an overturned bottle.

Prem smiled, trying to shake off the vice-like grip the eyes had on him. Eyes that appeared to be speaking a language, though uncommon, yet familiar to him. Like a recital by Kalamandalam Hyder Ali as he described the churning of the sea for nectar—the *amrit manthan*.

'Don't be afraid. My eyes are the only cool things in these

Kazhakazhi singer
a. 2006

yellow interiors, between these yellow walls. And they are not jaundiced,' Ramettan was enjoying his own joke, the timbre in the voice still comforting.

Prem's voice rose to say something. But he could only utter them months later when he met Ramettan the second time.

He had joined the group of students gathered in the college auditorium for the selections for the dance competition. He was a bit nervous. Not that he was ever to get over this stage fright. But this was a totally new place for him. Nervousness came from a fear of the unknown—new stage, new selectors, new environment. Though dancing was his first love, he was no veteran. That would happen only later, with some help from Ramettan.

'You inspire me,' Prem returned Ramettan's coy smile after his performance.

'You have been selected,' he told Prem.

Ramettan, he discovered, was also the college dance team's make-up man.

'There is no reason why you shouldn't have been selected,' he added after a moment's silence. That was reassuring.

In the days to come and after several practice sessions, Prem realized that Ramettan was always reassuring. There were moments when his limbs did not respond, when he felt that the floor beneath his feet would give way. But Ramettan would be there, gently stroking a lock of hair away from his face with a smile that packed words of comfort within it.

Ramettan was coolness personified. It was layered on his face like blankets in a hotel laundry. Remove one from the top and there is a similar one in white below. Impatient-cool. Angry-cool. Happy-cool. Sad-cool. It was as if his personality was just an expansion of the word.

Once they went for a film—John Abraham's *Amma* ✓ *Ariyan*. Prem recognized for the first time the resonance of human emotions in the sounds of the tabla. And his skin flinched when the fingers that played on the tabla were crushed beneath the boots of a policeman.

Perhaps to relieve him of the monstrosity of the situation, Ramettan said: 'Percussion attains perfection in the tabla. It fails with the mridangam, timila, edakka, chenda . . . They are all single instruments. The tabla, unlike them, is a twin object. One cannot be played without the other. Like emotion . . . an expression of it is futile without the complement of the receptor. Love, hate, pity diminish into thin air if expressed singularly. You need an other. One to the other and back. Like playing a tabla. It is not a soliloquy. It is dialogue between two. Like a marriage.'

The thought rested in Prem's mind for a long time. But both—the long cylindrical one and the other, short melon-like one—were instruments that were male in nature. How could they mate, he wondered. Yet the sounds were magical, in harmony, in unison.

Ramettan was not an exponent of such things, nor a master of classical dance. He had, Prem learnt, inculcated all he knew about dance from his father who was a make-up man at Kalamandalam.

Ramettan spoke lucidly on dance. And when he spoke he somehow emanated authority. 'The beauty of a performance lies not in what you have shown, but in what you have chosen not to,' Ramettan would tell him.

'The height of expression is not in letting go but in holding back. The secret is in holding back the lines, creases, crevices on your face, the curls in your fingers and toes, and not getting carried away.'

Prem never forgot those words of advice.

'I'll be away for a week,' he told his mother. He was to leave for the state-level dance competition at Thiruvananthapuram.

'I know,' she spoke with dissent.

Earlier she used to accompany him on such tours. It was something she cherished a lot. But this time he was going with the college team—perhaps an indication of the son drifting away.

She shrugged the thought away and said: 'Take care of yourself.'

Prem's team won the first prize in the group dance event. That night in the hotel room which they were sharing, Ramettan seemed very pleased. The individual event was to be held the next day. Prem was exhausted from the day's performance and the rigorous rehearsal. He lay down after a shower and soon slipped into a slumber.

Strong fingers rubbed his back. He turned his head and looked up.

'Lie down. I'll give you a massage,' Ramettan said. His massages had come good before every performance. It loosened the tired muscles and relaxed the mind.

'It was the lead you took at the right time that saved the day for us,' Ramettan said. His fingers had begun from the inside of Prem's toes and rounded off with the kneecap. Prem relived each moment of the day. His team had faltered in the midst of the recital. The other five members had miscued a step and moved ahead of the background vocals. With a twirl of his finger Prem had motioned the singers to repeat the last verse and stepped to the front to take the lead. No hitches, nothing out of tune, none noticed. As the chorus was repeated, his mates made up and the singers moved on to the next stanza.

Ramettan's hands kept up the languorous yet strong movements. Sprawled across the bed, Prem was like a hillock stretched across a barren landscape. He was tall, five feet ten inches, and unusually fair among the boys in his class. He had broad shoulders and a physique that would put any athlete to shame. It was his faintly feminine face that hid his masculinity. The wide lips, the shapely eyes and high cheekbones lent his persona a girlish mien. Otherwise he was man enough.

Ramettan's caressing spread like a mist over his body. The fingers curled under each curve. They even created a few where there were none. They had moved down his neck over his back down towards his buttocks. Prem's objections disappeared into the pillow.

The hands pressed the supple skin of his parted lobes. Dancing had made them more prominent. At times he had been embarrassed by the girlishness they gave his gait. A drop of sweat dropped onto his bare bottom. He did not know when his body had been shorn of the lungi that covered it.

The heat in the room engulfed his limbs. He turned around and pressed Ramettan close to his chest. That was to be his first act of adulthood.

As he wrapped himself around Ramettan, his eyes rested on the ceiling before shutting out consciousness.

He was dressed in silken white shining before the footlights. He was Mohini to Ramettan's Shiva. Prem's body drank in the philtre. He pressed and paced to Ramettan's beats. He floated from one corner of the stage to the other . . . following Ramettan's butterfly-like hands gliding through the air, his eyes uniting with Shiva's like the seductress Shwetambari.

The heat swam across his body. He could feel something moving up his thighs followed by an excruciating pain. A pain never known before. A pain similar, but much more pleasing than the one at the end of a long, intense performance. The pain turned rhythmic. The dance continued into the night.

Prem was overwhelmed with joy. Never had he known the ecstasy of exchange. What was it that emerged from the other being, the other body? What was it that made the pain so intensely enjoyable? Where had it been it hidden all these years? Was this love? Why hadn't he know this earlier?

At moments such as these, words become staccatto. Incomplete . . .

He said: 'Rametta . . .'

'You will do well, my beauty,' he replied, cool as ever. Panting, but cool.

That night, unlike others, did not evaporate, neither did it recede. Dawn was just an enjambment.

When Prem returned victorious from the championship, he had changed. Facing his mother, he was a heap of shame. But beneath the pile lay a little piece of velvety triumph. With trimmed sides and an initial stitched into a corner, that piece of cloth was one he would retain when he threw out the trash from the residence of his emotions. It was this cloth that he would use to wipe away the look of the boy from his face.

The cloth still exists. Not burned, not tarnished.

'It was in the newspapers,' Prem's mother said. 'They also carried your picture in Mohiniyattam vesham . . .'

Prem was not listening. He did not want to. The guilt of keeping something from his mother haunted him. It sealed his lips. There were moments when he wished to be alone. Then he sought refuge in the toilet. But that night the closed interiors of the four walls could not provide him solace. There was the piercing sound of droplets of water dripping from the tap . . . the humming of the tubelight . . . It was unbearable, but he thought hard. Through the sounds. Throughout the night. What was he? Why did he not, like other boys of his age, look at girls, talk about them, think about them? Occasionally he had been distracted by the movement beneath his mother's white blouse and he had cursed himself for those sinful skirmishes inside his mind. Why was he like this? Was it disinterest, morality bindings or sheer difference in the structure of his self? He tried to reconcile his mind, brain and body with his existence. He had always cursed his mother for the turmeric baths she gave him. But he had always savoured the feel of her fingers over his wet body and had admired his immaculate, smooth skin, taking pride in the fact that there was no hairy growth on his face. Never needed a shave. A moustache would have been a blotch on a white linen skin. But why? The thoughts continued . . .

He had relished each second of that night in the hotel. How he hated the morning for breaking the trance. For bringing him back, apart. For waking him up.

He did not go to college for many days at a stretch. And when he did, his path deliberately did not cross Ramettan's.

He heard from others that the soft-spoken, smiling clerk was not his usual self. One day it seems he had come made up to the office . . . And then he disappeared. They said he had shut himself inside his room. That he refused to see anyone. That he may be taken to a psychiatrist . . . to an asylum.

'He had come here,' Prem's mother said. 'You had gone to the market.' She was collecting wood for fire from the backyard. 'He was such a nice man. What happened to him all of a sudden?' she asked.

How could Prem tell her? How could Ramettan tell anyone?

She drew a deep sigh and continued: 'How long can a man continue all alone, with no one to look after him, no one to talk to . . . has to crack up . . .'

Prem had disappeared from beneath the coconut tree he was leaning against. It was now a habit for him to leave behind only a space where he was supposed to be. Even memories were a void. How could he remember that which was not his; be what he had no right to be?

The road on which he cycled lengthened into the evening. He sifted through the falling light to reach the doorstep of Ramettan's room. The room was open in invitation. As if Ramettan knew.

Prem stood at the door. The sight before him tied his feet to the ground.

The stage had been set on fire. Flames leapt up to meet the ceiling from all sides. In the centre, Ramettan was a column of frenzy. Shiva dancing the tandava. With the third eye open and burning he was consuming himself. The dancer and the dance . . . a denoument of destruction. He was prancing around on one leg with the other raised to his chest. His right hand held a small drum which tapered from both sides to the centre. Tied from the centre on long strings were beads that he was beating on. The damroo . . . a single piece instrument.

With the other he was shaking his member. Beating away ... jerking away ... fire in his eyes, fire in his limbs, fire on his body.

Prem turned around and ran, not knowing what to do. Or did he know exactly what he was doing? Was he afraid that the leaping flames might catch him too into their fold? He distanced himself from Ramettan's last act of self consummation ... self annihilation. As he ran, he kicked an empty tin of kerosene into a hollow compartment of the night.

Did it actually happen? Or had he imagined it all? He had no proof to verify his thoughts. The fire could have been captured by the camera. Later he tried to wish the thought away. Forgetting is not always the same as not remembering.

How could he look at those pictures of togetherness, holding them with hands of solitude, hands that were guilty of not having stretched out to hold another that had longed for them. Not long enough. Not longing enough? How could he remember moments he had no right to recollect?

He was still a loner—never able to come to terms with his inner urges, his sexuality. At thirty-eight, it no longer mattered. He was after all just another scientist succumbing to his own ambitious experiments.

And if someone asked why he had not married, he would reply with his boyish smile: 'Because my mother never asked me to.'

Prem's mother died twenty years ago. Two years later Ramettan died.

The Sweetest of All

Frank Krishner

The darkness enveloped me. I sat on the bench taking in the cool outside air. The long power cuts of Patna made remaining indoors unbearable, unless one lived in an apartment that ran a generator.

I was alone. What the hell, I was here in this godforsaken B-grade urban conglomeration of humans that passed for a city. And on a Saturday night to boot. Like the song goes, *I ain't got no buddy, I got some money 'cos I just got pay, all I need is someone to love me, I'm in an awful way*. I wasn't out there cruising or waiting to be chatted up. Sure, I heard about what happens on dark park benches late in the night, but the small playfield was deserted, and I was in no mood to be pawed by some Bhojpuri speaking, betel-juice squirting Neanderthal. To be honest, I was in no mood at all.

My mind was still in flashback mode, my heart about as light as a few tons of lead. Here I was, in exile, and all because of misreading the signs that litter the rocky road to relationships. In the music that is love, the eternal triangle has a nasty habit of sounding a harsh discordant note, and then the whole symphony comes crashing about your ears.

But it was another Saturday years ago when I was seventeen and on a hot August night, twenty-four-year-old Frank Richards lay beside me under a warm Ranchi sky. I was a pretty boy then. Blonde, slender, and with the kind of looks that turned my girlfriends green with envy.

Girlfriends, I had plenty of those, and that's just how they remained to this day. My family tree is cosmopolitan, with roots from the mountains of north-eastern India, where there is no segregation of the sexes, and little boys and little girls grow up into bigger boys and pretty young things without much embarrassment at all. I was sixteen when I discovered that guy-watching was a much more interesting sport than girl-watching. I would observe the sporting types on the school playfield, but end up wrapped up in a Mills and Boon after sunset. Real boys, they said, built model airplanes and played football in the rain. There were more than enough of them around.

Frank Richards. A guy doing his post-graduation in Political Science. We met during a Lion's Club debate. He was intense, a leftist. I was a devotee of the illustrious Ayn Rand. I worshipped Dylan and Neil Diamond. He was stuck on Jim Reeves, Engelbert Humperdinck and a rash of infra dig Hindi film songs. We argued, squabbled, drank gallons of fresh Assam tea in the little stall at Ward's Lake. And then he invited me to travel to Bihar and his native village on the Chhotanagpur plateau.

Richards was a swarthy-skinned adivasi with a barrel chest, a slim waist and a sprinkling of Anglo-Indian blood somewhere along the line. He had an ordinary kind of face and a rich baritone of a singing voice that was the delight of Mrs Lao, who conducted the Baptist church choir at Burra Bazaar. I attended the Grotto Church at Don Bosco Square, where old Father Bacchio commended me on the way I read from the scriptures. Shillong, with its churches and grottos, novenas and colourful ways inculcated from Italian missionaries, was often called the Rome of the East.

Ranchi, the summer capital and biggest town in south Bihar, hadn't escaped missionary zeal. Here too, churches raised their mighty spires. There was the great Catholic cathedral on Purulia road, the single spire of St. Paul's, the German battlements of the Lutheran church. During the days of the Great War, a Lutheran pastor, in an act of inspiration, loaded a small cannon and lodged a ball in the spire of St. Paul's, which can be seen to this day.

But unlike the North-East, the adivasis here made their own music in church—tribal tunes unchained by counterpoint or metronome. In'the village af Ormanjhi, Richards set aside his faded Levi's for a loincloth and rough fishing tackle, and fished near naked in the rain-fed waters of the turgid Swarnarekha.

That night, we were talking about the meaning of freedom. He rolled over, stared at my face in the moonlight, and said 'Are we really free? To do what our hearts really want to do?' And then he put his lips to mine and gave me the first taste of what I supposed heaven should have been. We made love, first hesitantly, then passionately, and then all over again.

Frank Richards became my lover, or rather, it was I who was in love. His family approved of the nice young 'foreign' friend from the North-East. On return to Shillong, we spent Saturday nights in his cramped bedroom, and went to Mass on Sunday to listen to sermons on temperance and the wrath of God. He even wrote me letters, and we went off for a honeymoon to Calcutta where we walked hand in hand down Park Street. A buddy of mine screamed, 'You two are behaving like bloody homos, men don't hold hands.' But we carried on regardless. It was holiday time and we were far from home. John and Yoko may have had their ballad a decade ago, but this was our time.

A discerning girlfriend from Ranchi went on a picnic with us, and told me later that night, 'He lusts after your skin. Mark my words, he's just showing you off to his rustic hometown pals like a trophy.' I laughed. I was in love. And how could she of the evil eye be the judge, she of the sallow skin and no-boyfriend reputation.

Frank Richards was my lover, and the girl with the evil eye could read the signs. He's not in your class, she pointed out. He doesn't know a meat knife from a fish fork, or a waltz from a tango. And have you noticed his awful dress-sense? So I took him to tea at Larsen's and to parties with the St.

Paul's crowd, where he supported the wall and I flashed around the dance-floor dazzling the dames in the best Travolta style. I was in the flush of Saturday night fever. He felt like a fish out of water, and the best Saturday nights, he said, were the two of us, the firelight, ruby wine, and take-out dinner from the Hong Kong Restaurant near Police Bazaar.

Here was I, the upper-class brat with a genuine English education, trying to play Henry Higgins. The subject of my attentions refused to let go of his squashed cabbage leaf. Instead of reading the signs, I decided to get to in touch with Richards's rustic roots.

I suffered the bumpy ride to a village in south Bihar, grinned at his toothless grandmother, tried to relish the coarse red rice and curried vegetables, and became an instant authority on Mundas and Oraons and the struggle for tribal rights. As I turned eighteen, I fancied myself beside this great supporter of the downtrodden, fighting the landlords and the system shoulder to shoulder.

And then I caught him smooching a particularly ugly and smelly adivasi wench, with heaving bosom and rounded buttocks, bad breath and all.

On the long journey back to civilization, he gave me the line, 'If only you were a girl.' The line wasn't new. A year ago, back on the train from Calcutta, he had told me that it would have been wonderful had I been a woman and we could have belonged to one another 'completely'.

'You should have been a woman.' This is the classic cliché that the men in Bihar use on their lover boys. It is a psychological mantra to convince himself he is still heterosexual, and to perpetuate the myth that his passive partner is somehow less than a man. There can be no crueller cut, especially if the boy is slightly built, beautiful, and terribly in love with the man. But no warning lights flashed in the sky. I decided to become a woman.

My mother looked as though I had belted her over the head with the Shillong Peak. I told her I wanted a sex change operation. She couldn't believe her ears, but accompanied me dutifully to the family quack. He asked me to drop my underpants, took one look and said, 'There's nothing the matter with him.'

That settled it for my mother. 'Don't ever tell me about such nonsense again, the very idea!' she sniffed.

But I wanted a second opinion from the best doctor in town. Richards came alone with me. Dr Chaudhary examined me thoroughly and said in a loud voice, 'My dear, you are a healthy male teenager, with all your equipment in fine working order. Get this transsexual nonsense out of your head. The operation will not only be bloody expensive, it's just short of a hoax. What's wrong with living in a homosexual relationship with your friend? It's done all over the world. Believe me,' he said, staring long and hard at Richards, 'don't rush into something you'll regret later. If your lover wants a woman, what's he doing in your bed?'

'If you only were a girl.' The coin dropped firmly in place. 'I'm not a girl,' I told him. 'I'm a guy. If that woman can give you a hundred per cent satisfaction, it's fine. But if you want me, I'm a cute guy, but not a woman.' Back in Shillong, he came over to my place to patch things up. I told him that I would be very busy for the next three months. He tried calling up once or twice, and then the phone stopped ringing. He had completed his studies and returned to Bihar.

I continued to correspond with his paralysed father, a lovable man who strummed a mean guitar from his sick bed.

Many years later, I received an envelope with a familiar scrawl. Richards had spotted my column in a national newspaper. It was a short note of congratulations. 'You always had wanted to be a journalist,' he wrote. He had got a job in the Railways, was posted in Lucknow. I sent him a noncommittal, polite reply. We exchanged Christmas cards for a couple of years after that, and then Frank Richards sort of shunted away into the distance.

I sat there on the bench in the darkness, thinking about users and abusers.

But it wasn't Frank Richards who was on my mind on that park bench. I was thinking of the Saturday night I met Rajendra. A full room swinging with Pink Floyd and bodies in syncopation. Pretty girls, handsome guys, plenty of beer. A typical wild north-eastern bang-up that happens whenever the crowd at the North Eastern Hill University campus can manage to shanghai a location. I waded through the jungle of flailing arms and swinging torsos to a backroom to find the host, and there in the circle of light, strumming a guitar sat this divine apparition. The room had about two dozen people, quiet and attentive. The voice was haunting, melodious, the quality of bitter chocolate. He was singing a particularly haunting Nepali ballad. The lover was telling his beloved, 'I wish you well as you travel the perilous path through the jungle of life'.

He was singing with his head bowed. And when the song finished, raised his eyes and looked straight into my very soul. He smiled at me and nodded, and then began killing me softly, knowingly. *'Euta manchay ko maya le kotee farka paradesha zingagi maa'* . . . This popular song written by the Nepali music legend Narayan Gopal brought a round of applause. But the guy wasn't taking his eyes off me. He was ruggedly handsome, a veritable Bruce Lee with a golden voice to match. And oh sweet Jesus! He was actually singing this song to me. 'It's strange how my life has changed just because of the love of a single person', the song said.

Then he handed the guitar to somebody else, and came straight at me. My head came up to his shoulder. He gave his shiny black shoulder-length hair a shake. He took both my hands in his and said, 'I'm Rajendra, you must be Mark. You sing English songs, don't you?'

A girl gushed, 'Rajen, what a voice! How about coming outside for some beer?' he disentangled her fingers from his arm with a gentle firmness and said, 'You see, we musicians are talking serious business. Some other time, okay?'

He put his arms around me and steered me out of the

room and into the whirl of dancing bodies. He spun me around and began to jive. Our host, Andrew Sohliya, was the emcee. 'Hey, you guys, break it up,' he said. 'There are many girls just waiting for you guys to pick them up.'

Rajen smiled broadly as he countered, 'Emcee, you piss off. Mark and I are doing some dirty dancing. Come back later. Why don't you pick up some of those pretty girls and get laid in the meantime?' and when the music mellowed and the lights went low, and Don Williams sang 'We are the loving proof, beyond the shadow of doubt', he held me close and said, 'You're coming back with me. You can't get rid of me, you know.'

He led me outside under the cold stars and kissed me. And you bet I heard those violins. I knew that this had to be love. Rajen was nineteen. I was twenty-one. But he had more confidence, dash and drive than three of me. In the years that followed, it was Rajen who encouraged me to write stories, who arranged for a Kathmandu group to set some of my songs to music, and to remind me that I should be true to myself.

We went together to his home in south Sikkim. A family of four brothers and a sweet old mother who instantly took to me and called me 'saila'—her fourth child, because there was a baby brother in the family whose position was now demoted to fifth! In the years that followed, I pursued my career in journalism, while Rajen completed his studies. We were always in touch, and together during vacations or whenever possible. He finished his studies and joined as a junior engineer in the Sikkim Power Department.

One day he called me up. 'My mother is arranging a wedding. Mine. I've seen the girl and like her a lot. Would you like to see her? Come up to Sikkim next week, we'll go together to Kathmandu.'

I had an assignment in Delhi. Here was my partner telling me to approve of what? A second spouse? I bit back my tears and asked him firmly, 'Do you really like this girl?'

'Oh, yes, she's great. A veterinary doctor as well.'

'Then go ahead,' I said. Grown men don't cry, I told myself.

And I took up an assignment in Bihar. The toughest assignment a journalist can get, they said. A state where killing and looting takes place everyday.

But as I sat there in the darkness, in the midst of an indefinite power cut, I re-read a letter in my mind. Rajen had written: Dearest M, we've got a son. We've named him Rohit Mark. Vinita is posted at Melli town, while I am at Namche, in the old house. Do consider coming over to Namche. You must write that book on Lepcha folklore, and Rohit must know his uncle . . . With all my love, always, your one and only, R.

And I also reviewed my answer. 'I will definitely come for a week when Vinita is back in town and I can meet your family together. I do want to meet my nephew. My love to all of you, especially your dear wife and little Rohit. Your brother, Mark.' I didn't know whether Rajen had ever told his wife about us. The last thing I wanted was to have little Rohit's world blown apart.

'Excuse me,' a voice broke into my thoughts. The neon light overhead flickered into life. 'Would you mind if I sat down here a moment?' He was tall and not bad looking at all. 'Suit yourself,' I said. 'I was waiting out the power cut. Now that the lights are back, I'll get back to my flat.'

'Actually, I was strolling around for the same reason. It's too bloody hot. Say, I can give you a ride back to your flat. It's number 701, isn't it?'

'How do you know?'

'Look, you know the Malhotras in 699? I'm a distant cousin. Doing fashion designing at Bombay. I'm down for a short spell. Say, why don't we go for an ice cream?'

I thought of Rajen as I climbed into the white Maruti. Praful—that was the chap's name—turned on the stereo. Doctor Hook droned on and I mentally sent it out to Rajen:

It wasn't my first love.
It wasn't my last,
but yours was the sweetest of all.

Knowing Your Place

Ian Iqbal Rashid

1. *Passage from Africa / A Pass to India*

i)

I know these places awkwardly
like the bundles I take with me
that soon I hope
will float beside me constantly.

These places are sudden
with absence of metaphor.
Like the absences my parents live with:
an ebbing of fluency
a poverty of words for white
unable to dream in snow.

ii)

They were sent to a place without light.
Home is *the dark continent*.
An immovable mass keeping us separate
blocking the view between our stories.

Did they leave
as I leave now

carrying papers
in case they might vanish?

iii)

Vanish and merge
emerging as people we've never known, unfinished.
Like stories with disappeared endings
told by old photos and older women
bent by time and disapproval.

Stories fading
at their salt water edges
curling, crisp with hints.

iv)

Stories which hold me often
whose endings
like fists are snake-tight
over-eager embraces
that open to caress me, now and again

now, mocking my obsession
this open hand of a story
its teasing misshapen fingertip of a subcontinent.

And I leave
reading one of two epic poems
governing a struggle
that will not vanish

gripping a line
that zips open a sky of myth

exposing its soft
little boy's belly

leaving stiff vestments behind,
leaving an anger behind
with the buildings we are tunneling by with a roar

leaving for a place that knows me well
    as a cell
        under attack
            knows its virus.

Autobiography

Hoshang Merchant

My first memory of my mother is of her moving around my sickroom. Her hair was down to her waist. She wore a green kimono.

My first photograph shows me seated in the lap of 'granny', an elderly neighbour. I am frowning, my hands cup my face. The yellow print dress was my favourite. Father took the photograph in the late afternoon sun. My grandparents disapproved of my parents' marriage since mother was a divorcee. I sat in Grandfather's lap and pulled his beard. Once I wore his priest's cap as he napped.

The barred window to which I clung before being sent off to school is still there. I would sit in class with my elder sister. Father was remote: a young face in dark glasses looking over my crib during malaria fevers. I had 'incurable' eczema. At birth I bled hours from the severed umbilicus. Once I had an insect-bite on the penis: Mother beat a 'confession' out of me, Father carried me to a doctor. During haircuts I wept and was given caraway seed candies. I hated boarding school and was brought home in days.

Arrival of a new baby: Father placed collyrium, rose water, rice, a silver rupee, a vigil lamp, a portrait of Zoroaster, pen, ink and paper in a 'puja' tray. The goddess of good fortune would write the newborn's future. I would sit in my sister's crib and feed her milk out of a bottle. Mother lay in a hospital room amid a scent of phlox. When we left her with the tiny new baby she pined.

I was the only boy in school. Mother had decided I wouldn't swear or be rough. I sang, danced, cooked and sewed. But I could not thread needles. I hated English but loved History. At home I dressed in a sari and sang and danced under the cherry tree with sister. My parents did not like this.

One day a man came with a tin box which hung from his neck. Atop the box was a rag doll whose hands he manipulated with a string tied to his toe. For an anna each, children could press an eye to one of the two windows of this magic box and see views:

> Dilli ka Durbar dekho
> Agra ka Taj Mahal dekho
> Kathputli ka naach dekho
> Vyjanthimala dekho
> Dekho bacche dekho

Only his commentary did not have anything to do with the images in the magic lantern.

At seven I became a Zoroastrian. I addressed fervent prayers to a rosy-cheeked man whose blond locks coiled around him like snakes. His turban was like Grandfather's. I went to school, returned, prayed after dinner and fell asleep instantly. In Zoroaster's huge fire temple portrait I saw only his feet. I wore a sacred girdle round my waist: 'to separate the lofty from the gross'.

We moved from our two-room apartment to a vast bungalow by the sea, with a fernery and a wild bamboo garden. The house was green and built athwart a hill. At ebb tide I saw rocks come up from the water. I dreamt of lost continents. It rained for days. The brain-fever bird. Jasmine. The old chandelier dropped crystals which we collected.

Dropping us off at school each morning Father tarried at the shopping centre exchanging compliments with the pharmacist, the laundry girls, the store keepers. He was known by his six-cylinder Morris with a Great Britain licence plate. Doors were opened for him as he arrived late for work, at his traditional hour. As he went through the mills' printing, sizing or dyeing departments he hauled up idling workers, his fits of temper and abuses ringing from the tin roofs. Then he was served breakfast: eggs in butter, without pepper. Lunch from the mess was rounded off by a nap in a low chair. A masseur suspended him six inches from earth daily. He walked better when let down again. A shower in the specially installed shower stall and fresh hankies and cologne to beat the heat was followed by the court for labour problems with slaps meted out to offenders. Then came flowers from the company gardens: carnations, cannas, roses, which Mother arranged for evening tea. But Father had come up the hard way. After repudiating an inheritance he started off again washing dyestuff drums for seventy-five rupees a month. Now he received pay-offs from dyestuff dealers for business favours.

During summer vacations in Poona we saw the ex-Maharani Chimnabai Gaekwad of Baroda drive by on the Bund in a 'thirties' Rolls-Royce. She wore chiffon and pearls and as the car rolled by at five m.p.h. we saw the old face, impassive and white, laced with wrinkles. Her equally impassive Indian chauffeur tooled her home around sunset. Mother told us she had poisoned the Gaekwad's heir to further the chances of her own son.

On a visit to an old palace we saw the royal bed where a dog had littered.

My parents quarrelled. A policeman stationed to ward off bootleggers often intervened. Grandfather sided with Father, menfolk with menfolk.

A court clerk arrived with a paper for my mother to sign. She wept. Father wasn't home. He'd sued for divorce. Eden fled. We were herded in the six-cylinder Morris and taken to a lawyer. Could we choose between our parents? Our parents reconciled. Mother bought an emerald and crystal vase for her roses, Father, a gramophone and LPs of waltzes.

I went to a boys' school. I didn't play cricket. The lady teacher liked me, so did the Jesuit. A phone call for me: 'Why did you volunteer to go to a boarding school?' Father had sued for divorce a second time. That recess I was particularly alone. When Father came to fetch me for boarding school I refused to go. I started taking the suburban train fourteen kilometres to school. I recited a prepared speech before a judge: 'If I'm separated from Mother, I'd die.'

My parents were reconciled again. I saw them kissing. He was in trouble at work.

On the train a stranger 'protected' me in the rush. He didn't let go of me even when the crowds lessened. I didn't believe my friend who told me the stranger's intent.

A group of boys gathered around a *Playboy* centrefold of a nude in a red veil. I was uninterested. The big boy of our class displayed his member. The Jesuit broke up our gathering. I confessed to Mother. I had wet dreams. I learnt the word 'overflow'. Mother was disbelieving.

Every Saturday afternoon Father took me out to lunch: fruit salad and ice cream. A girl joined us. I liked her as I was always alone. Aunts, uncles, cousins, grandparents I knew none, nor playmates. Mother questioned me: Was she young? Was she fair? I fabulated, played to my mother's worst expectations of the girl, pitiful and indignant that Mother should have a rival. We never saw the girl again.

At school I was shy. I hated mathematics. I liked memory-drawing. The art master touched me once but I moved away. I took up dramatics. All the female roles came to me: Martha in a Christmas pageant, the mother in *Amahl and the Night-strangers*, the wife in *These Cornfields* played as if she were Lady Macbeth in a veil since wigs and falsies were taboo. I won a prize for my portrayal of a henpecked husband. I had a beard coming.

Mother was arthritic. Now she was crippled and walked with crutches. At the nursing home a rat gnawed at her in her sleep. She could not afford another place. Father had left yet again: Case number 36 of '63. Things were beyond me.

Mother was locked out of the house. She cut her arm on the glass door. She defended herself and struck Father on the forehead with a stone. For the first time I saw Father weep. A servant attended to him. The servant restrained my mother from going to the sea to drown herself. There was a curse on my mother, doomed to lamentation on each auspicious occasion. Dinners were thrown on the floor. We were startled out of bed, lights went up, Mother screamed all night for help from neighbours. I went to the police with my mother in nightclothes. I did not know why my parents married, nor did the school psychiatrist who asked me to be a curator.

My younger sister and I drew blood from each other. I decided not to be a surgeon when my own blood sickened me. As children, elder sister and I had excluded younger sister from 'heaven': though beautiful and lucky she was 'tainted', we said.

Elder sister and I decided to play 'house'. We partitioned the house and posted a sign 'Hippo, stay out' to antagonize Mother, who peered through the ventilators now and then. We went out on food 'raids'. Our house within a house did not last long. Father accused me of sleeping with sister.

My effeminacy antagonized Father. During their fights I stood square between mother and him. Disturbed by my sign of maleness he aimed at my genitals.

It was I who touched the man on the suburban train. He came in his trousers. He took me to a carpenter's attic. Amid sawdust he penetrated me. I felt pain and loss. He offered me a candy.

Picking up a man for Saturday afternoons: I would be at the railway station at eight each morning at the foot of the bridge to see men descending. I would first see feet, then groin, torso, face in that order.

A stray lock, a weak eye, flared nostrils, a paunch—something would have to be attractive. I would follow him into the overcrowded compartment. After the initial accidental strokes and brushes I would have the genitals in my hands. This was done wordlessly for days each morning; finally I would be invited home. Sometimes from an evening train home we would end up on the beach. I thought I was cursed to the orgasmless life. I looked up 'homosexual' in the dictionary. I didn't sleep with the same man twice for fear of scandal. But my secret was out. I confessed to my elder sister who told Mother, who complained to Father who wept by the sea, sent me to a therapist and asked me to be a man.

Then he tried tenderness with me. I had fallen in love with a classmate my last year of school. I kept chaste for him, started an adolescent diary, dreamt of running away with him and living with him forever. It did not happen. I tried suicide. Pills. Nothing happened. Father, tired and remorseful, asked if we hadn't heard of the Chinvat bridge in the Zoroastrian heaven that people who commit suicide can never cross. Daena (conscience), for that was also Mother's name, would meet me and say, 'I am ugly for your action has made me so.' She was to be a fair maiden.

My college friend fell in love with sister. From her I learnt how to pine, quarrel, show mock anger, lure and finally attain. The boy's father ran a ferris wheel at the fiesta of Mary of the Mount. Each September with Mother we would climb to Mary's church past shops selling votive limbs, legs, arms, even babies in wax to be offered at the altar. Mary was said to have come out of the sea. She trod on a serpent or on a moon-crescent. Ave Maria. Mother's birthday fell then: first of the five ritual days for the dead preceding the Zoroastrian harvest rites. Mother on losing a child had been promised many more by Mary in a dream. Now Mother was legless, Father was gone. We were alone. I lost god.

Father brought us *Advise to Adolescents*: 'Do not masturbate dear children, it will blind you.'

'There is a river whose water may never fall on earth, a tree whose roots are above and whose fruits are to be reverted before they fall.'

The untouchable people had washed toilets for

generations. She was customarily let in through a window on which rested a small wooden ladder. Mother was the first one to let her come in to work through the front door. Now and then she chatted about her family with Mother, squatting on the floor and sipping tea from a broken china cup set aside for her. Like everyone in Bombay she wanted to get rich quick in the film industry. Her favourite fantasy role was of a drunk—she probably ran a stall in her shantytown hut. Her wealth she wore—two gold earrings so heavy that they had torn the ear lobes.

The other servant was a Brahmin from north India. He wore a pigtail and the sacred thread. Though a vegetarian he helped out with the cooking of meat at home. He was a mill labourer brought home by Father. Mother suspected him of being a spy; that he was mercenary there's no doubt. But when he filled the water pots at dawn he sang loudly from the Tulsi Ramayana, old old songs that had seen him through many births, marriages and deaths.

Towards me Mother was unforgiving. I was not to enter her room, nor use her comb, nor her chair or bed. Acne was venereal. She did not forgive Father either: he was spoilt, his grandfather had given him money to visit whores, he was lust-driven. 'Homosexual' was equivalent to 'hermaphrodite' or 'eunuch'. Mother called weak men 'hijra'.

Hijras cross-dressed, moved about in packs begging and singing. Though flat-chested some carried infants to mimic motherhood. Their voices deep, their mannerisms slutty, they would display themselves if their performances weren't adequately rewarded. Some were ritually castrated at a mother-goddess's temple to be able to withstand women, to be the goddess herself. They were associated with Friday, fertility rites, weddings and births.

I'd go on long walks through Bombay. The pavements were jammed with hawkers. Pornography was sold wrapped in yellow cellophane and routinely titled *Kama sutra—An Art and a Science*. I'd walk the arcades under the office buildings around Flora Fountain, go past the statue of King George on a black steed, walk up to the water at Apollo Pier where pigeons fed from the hat of the Prince of Wales.

My patience ran out: I once shook Mother by her shoulder, making her lose her balance. She broke a hip joint and never recovered. It was then that I tried suicide.

The trial was upon us. Father charged desertion; Mother, cruelty. I stole billets-doux from my father's cupboard: 'I came running . . .' Sister discovered them in bed. 'To love is no sin', the girl wept. Later sister tried suicide rather than testify against a father she loved. The girl was unintelligent, uncultured, unbeautiful. What did Father see in her?

Mother was once vibrant and accomplished. She sang and played the sitar—among the first bourgeois girls to do so, since dance and music in old India were for prostitutes. During the freedom movement she wore homespun cotton. She spoke to us of the astral body and the Lord to come. Why then had she given it all up? She was once beautiful. We found her tiny swimsuit in an old trunk. She was once offered a movie role, or so she always said. Her father castigated her vanity. A silent movie star, a neighbour, though disfigured in an accident had photographs from her youth. Mother was too poor to afford a wedding portrait.

In quieter days Mother would gather us around her and recite 'The Forsaken Merman' and weep. Among her letters we discovered a photograph of a little girl we didn't know. Mother had abandoned this girl because of us. Years later we saw the girl, a woman now, with long hair to her waist and wide eyes. Mother was not allowed to attend her daughter's wedding.

The wedding ceremony: The wife is separated from her husband by a screen, man from woman, matter from spirit. They are bound for life by the strength of a thread circled seven-fold, a charmed circle of marriage. They are showered with rice. Sister bowed before Grandfather. Dressed in white and gold she wept.

My mother felt guilt for forsaking her husband and child.

A Zoroastrian versed in Burmese magic had been contracted by my paternal grandmother to separate Father from Mother. Enchantments to fight enchantment: a charm only works if the victim is first told about it.

Since I wasn't allowed to go to the cinema in childhood, I now started seeing all the old films. I particularly remember Nargis, photographs of Monroe, the young Novak in *Picnic, The Children's Hour*: 'Look, I'm a freak with six fingers!' Without knowing Bengali I sat through all of Satyajit Ray. I noticed the difference between the person and the screen personality in several Bombay stars. Kalpana, a neighbour, seemed more beautiful off-screen. Our disbelieving maid announced the star's breasts were foam rubber. I attended Kathak recitals, wrote poems.

Indians are divided fourteen times into fourteen languages. I studied my mother tongue first. English was taught under the rubric of 'General Knowledge' in the vernacular schools. Hindi is spoken in Bombay's film world. The school syllabi were heavy with Victorian poetry. Babu English was the norm for daily intercourse. The Western-educated Indian of my age has no memory of any language other than English. If 'Black' expression is now the rage, India's foreign-educated elite lacks a language for it. It is true that I curse in Gujarati but it is equally true that I dream in English. Literary prose is more of a drawback to the Indian writer in English rather than his lack of Indian languages.

One day, a little misshapen old lady followed my father into the house. Mother was hospitalized. A younger woman followed: my paternal grandmother and aunt. I had seen them for the first time at eighteen. They had forgiven Father now that his marriage was irretrievably broken. My grandmother, an educated young widow, had become a small bent shape harboring a twenty-five-year-old unforgiveness based on her 'principles'. I saw her one other time: 'To America! To America! To study English,' said my father's mother. It was the second time I had seen her. She was a devotee of the Meher Baba. When Father in his childhood fell ill his mother, a physician's widow, took him to the Baba for faith-healing. Only an emergency operation saved his life. I was fearful of the mysterious Baba in childhood, dreaming of him before falling off to sleep. I had seen the barred cave where he meditated. My grandmother, a jeweller's daughter, was to leave her legacy to Baba. Father would not be forgiven.

The trial started. I accompanied Mother to the Bombay High Court: dark stone buildings full of pigeon droppings from the rafters, with post-Raj liveried doormen, cloaked lawyers and their devils. Accusations of influence-peddling, deception ·in marriage and divorce. All the old hurts, wounds photographed, catalogued, filed away, now played upon in the hands of paid lawyers. Mother refused an out-of-court settlement. She wanted 'justice', a public validation of the worth of her tribulations; he, a public absolution of his guilt, a public statement of male power. My old grandfather weeping silently; sent away. They had certified my maternal grandmother insane, had her beaten with chains to drive out the devil in her. The same forces once before judged my mother guilty of deserting a man she was forced to marry in an arranged marriage and whom she had the courage to leave. The same forces now called her a man-wrecker, an insane person, an undutiful wife, a thief of her husband's wealth, guilty of beating back a man who assaulted her. I testified on Mother's behalf. We had become too poor to eat amid plenty. My parents who were married in seventy-five rupees spent thousands on their divorce. The trial had become mother's raison d'être: she spent years writing brief upon brief. Then she died.

I gave language and history lessons. My students had interesting mothers: one loved her brother-in-law; another, an ex-baronet's wife, paid up her losses at the races by selling off inherited Chinese ivory—her house was full of pedestals on which statues once stood; a third, a Jew married to a Hindu film director had a daughter from a previous marriage who dreamt of a career in the movies; yet another, the jobless wife of a successful executive, concocted a life for herself as a stewardess.

Mother reprimanded both my girlfriends and the men when they called me on the phone at home.

At nineteen I met Placid, twenty-five, bronze complexioned, of middle build but athletic, with light eyes and a prominent mole on his cheek. He was a nuclear physicist. We met in a train and kept trysts each Tuesday morning. Sounds of children outside would waft into the room. He would await me wearing nothing but a towel wrapped around his waist, open the door to his one-room dwelling and sneak me in. I wrote him poems, the scent of his sandalwood oil stayed with me for days. Once while he was visiting his family in south India I turned up at his door and was seen by a cousin of his. I was severely admonished later by Placid.

I met a chef. The monsoons had set in. My friend wore a raincoat and dangled a cigarette from the corner of his rather full mouth like Bogart. We took a cab to the sea and awaited nightfall. We made love: throat, chest, navel, thigh. The sky grew dizzy: 'What happened?' The cabbie watched the whole scene from a parapet. I was twenty, I had met the man in the train at fourteen.

Mother offered me a holiday in Kashmir. A Kashmiri curio dealer had me locked in his offices and beaten, calling me an 'Indian' all the while because I had accidentally scratched one of his curios while handling it. I did not realize it then but I had internalized the pleasure of being beaten while watching all my mother's suffering.

During a famine, after waiting hours in a ration queue I was charged the blackmarket price. 'Ask your father how he got rich,' said the grain dealer.

I asked Mother to leave me her papers. She refused: 'You will malign me.'

I read about a liberation movement among American homosexuals—the Mattachine Society. 'Mattachine' in

Spanish means 'puppet'. After securing admission to a California college, Father and I struck a bargain: I was to sign over to him everything in return for a year's fees. I signed transfers for half an hour. I felt free, I thought of never returning again.

I reported a boy-servant to the police for petty theft. I sat there listening to his cries as they tried to beat a confession out of him at the police station.

Mother appeared in the doorway on crutches: 'Do not leave. I'm about to die.'

Love is a constant terror of loss.

The first loss of earth is loss of home.

Afterword

Hannah Arendt writing in *The Human Condition* after the War said that a human being's greatest authenticity came from her experience, her suffering.

Author/authority—the two are related. Post-structuralism has announced the death of the author. Philosophies need authors: the Gospel according to St. John. This is my testament.

It is fashionable to blame mothers for homosexuality in sons. The fact is weak husbands make for strong wives who breed weak sons who in turn become weak husbands. Strindberg catalogues this in *The Father* which is wrongly considered a misogynistic play. This is specially true for the Parsi society today.

'For whom will you write your book?' the anti-intellectual working class American gays taunted me at a '70s liberation rally. 'For the gays,' I'd then said. 'But the gays already know it all.' ('They're living it all,' was what was meant.) Then I said: 'I'll write for the straights.' I still think gays can use this book better than straights. Liberation, like charity, begins at home.

It should be obvious from this survey that 'gay' in India is not an ethic, not a religion, not a sub-culture, not a profession, not a sub-caste. Yet it is all-present, all pervasive, ever practised and ever secret. It comes upon you in unexpected places, in unexpected faces. It is shame, guilt, subversion; for some new-fangled ones even their honour and pride. Homosexuals are largely unorganized and blend with the crowd. Hence homosexuality is unspoken about, unaccepted, a danger to the homosexual and the non-homosexual alike. Unlike 'hijras' the gays do not have a local habitation or even a name. No word exists yet for the homosexual in any of India's languages. No one in any class wants to own up to it. It is a movement with a thousand colours. Yet it is distasteful to many and many consider it tasteless though it has its very pungent odours and colours. There are laws against it but they have not been enforced for a hundred years. Yet no one wants to bell the cat, no one wishes to repeal a practically defunct law. Parliament has gone to sleep over the Bill moved by some Delhi gays. The Culture studies establishment does not want to own up to gay studies and the village school teacher may not play Plato especially if he is one. Gays get married (to women), get humiliated or mutilated (as hijras) almost daily with a sickening frequency and some homosexuals masochistically seek out humiliation several times a day. Riyad Vinci Wadia says in *Parsiana* (Dec. 1996, p.24) that '50 million Indian men have sex with other men'. There is no remedy, therapy, counselling for any one of these many millions of people. Homosexual men are accused of harbouring AIDS though it is the heterosexual population that is the main carrier that spreads the disease in Asia. AIDS is just one more new reason to hate the gay.

Recent genetic theory gives a genetic basis to homosexuality. Some future Hitler now can happily stamp out all human difference by aborting foetuses testing positive for the 'gay gene'! Homosexuality has always been a happy hunting ground for fascists of all hues.

Proust called homosexuality 'a freemasonry of the damned': a homosexual could make a grand tour of Europe once without once paying hotel rent, so numerous was the sisterhood. In San Francisco I called Castro Street its 'gay ghetto' with 'fags living on top of dogs living on top of fags'! In the bourgeois West the homosexual is accepted as a happy credit-card-carrying, tax-paying bourgeois with just another kink in the head or in the bed. That too is just one more bourgeois plot to make us disappear.

July 1999   Hoshang Merchant

Biographical Notes

Adil Jussawalla was born in Bombay in 1940. He studied and worked abroad—mostly in London and Oxford—between 1957-69, with two longish stays in Bombay during that period. He returned to India in 1970 and decided to stay on. He is the author of two books of poems—*Land's End* (1962) and *Missing Person* (1976).

Ashok Row Kavi was born in 1947, in Bombay. He graduated from the University of Bombay with an honours degree in Chemistry. Subsequently, he dropped out of engineering college and switched to theology. He acquired a post-graduate diploma in theology from the Ramakrishna order and started his career as a journalist in 1974 with the *Indian Express*, and was the chief reporter with the *Free Press Journal* from 1984 to 1989. In 1991, he founded *Bombay Dost*, India's first gay magazine.

Belinder Dhanoa was born in Shillong. She studied English Literature at the North Eastern Hill University before going on to take a Masters in Art Criticism from the Faculty of Fine Arts in Baroda. She is working at present towards a Ph.D in Comparative Arts at the University of Rochester, New York. Belinder Dhanoa has written several books for children.

Bhupen Khakhar (b. 1935) is a qualified chartered accountant who after retirement distinguished himself as a painter and teacher of the Baroda School. The Baroda School led by Khakhar and Gulam and Neelima Sheikh is characterized by city-scapes peopled by men and women engaged in scenes of daily living. Though trained in Western techniques and languages, Bhupen Khakhar writes in his native tongue, Gujarati.

Dinyar Godrej (b. 1965) grew up in Indore, India. His formal education was at St. Xavier's College, Bombay and St. Anne's College, Oxford. For his informal education he is indebted to his family and some exceptional friends. He has worked, among other things, as a freelance writer and teacher.

Firaq Gorakhpuri née Raghupati Sahay(1896-1982), Urdu's foremost poet, was an influential teacher of English Romantic poetry for decades at Allahabad University. In his lifetime, it was an open secret that Firaq was a homosexual. It was also a well-known fact that he never wrote a gay line. The ghazal included in this anthology, taken from the literary periodical *Sabras* (Hyderabad), is the only 'gay poem' of Firaq's the editor could find.

Firdaus Kanga first appeared in print in *Kaiser-i-Hind*, a now defunct Bombay Parsi rag, with an evocative piece on a male childhood friend. Then came the success of *Trying to Grow*, his courageous confession of being gay, the break with his now horrified but till then supportive Parsi mother and the success with the liberal English establishment for whom it is *de riguer* to love an outsider, for Kanga is an outsider thrice over, immigrant, handicapped, gay—and an artist.

Frank Krishner is based in Patna and writes for the *Times of India*.

Gyansingh Shatir (b. 1935) was born to a Sikh carpenter family in Gurdaspur, Punjab. Urdu was the official language in pre-Partition Punjab. Shatir's Urdu which is self-taught has a lot of Punjabi idiom in it. An engineer by training, Shatir took eighteen years to write his autobiography of 650 pages which brings him up to the eighteenth year of his life. Joycean in its Urdu-Punjabi coinages, it is an Indian *Portrait of the Artist as a Young Man*. He won the Sahitya Akademi award in 1998.

Ian Iqbal Rashid (b. 1965) is a creative and critical writer who has been published by many magazines and journals in the UK and in North America. He also reviews literature and film regularly for the British Broadcasting Corporation (BBC) Radio 4's *Kaleidoscope*. His poetry publications include *Black Markets, White Boyfriends and Other Acts of Elision, Song of Sabu* and *The Heat Yesterday*.

Iqbal Mateen is a retired State Government employee and lives in Nizamabad. The book *Sheltered Flame* (*Cherag-e-Tehe Daman*) was denied State recognition because of its controversial subject of a prostitute and her gay son.

Kamleshwar is one of the best-known contemporary fiction writers writing in the vernacular in India. He has won numerous awards for his work. The Hindi novel, *The Street with Fifty-Seven Lanes*, created a furore when it first appeared in 1976 because of its homosexual overtones.

Madhav G. Gawankar is in his thirties and lives in Dapoli on the Konkan coast. His gay stories have been accepted in many mainstream Marathi publications.

Mahesh Dattani is India's only English playwright writing currently for the stage. His plays include *Dance Like a Man, Bravely Fought the Queen, Final Solutions, Tara* and *On a Muggy Night in Mumbai*. Dattani teaches in the drama workshop at Portland University, Oregon, every summer. He has his own company, Playpen, and lives in Bangalore.

Manoj Nair is a young journalist working with the *Hindustan Times* in New Delhi.

Namdeo Dhasal is a Dalit Marathi poet. He recently left Ambedkar's party to join the Shiv Sena.

Owais Khan works for an MNC computer major, as a Business Manager. Officially named Mohammed Owais Khan by his doting, yet domineering single mother, he took his time before he called himself gay. Since then apart from starting, helping, and running gay support groups in Hyderabad, New Delhi, Bangalore, Mumbai and Calcutta, he has initiated LGBT India, the nation-wide network of LGBT groups. In his remaining time, apart from writing poetry, he is also writing a novel. He is currently based in Bangalore.

R. Raj Rao was born in Mumbai. His father was from Rajahmundry in Andhra Pradesh and his mother a Sindhi. Raj Rao first studied commerce, then wrote an MA thesis for Bombay University on the concept of beauty in Tagore and Whitman, under Nissim Ezekiel. He then worked at National College, Bandra as a lecturer.

Raj Rao was later appointed Reader in Pune University and sent abroad (to Leeds) to study Caribbean Literature. He has several published poems and stories to his credit.

R. Raj Rao also writes plays and is currently working on a biography of Nissim Ezekiel.

Rakesh Ratti's poetry is a heart-rending example of the anxiety of a homosexual living in the diaspora. For an Indian homosexual emigrant to America, life can be extremely difficult for he is part of a minority within a minority within a minority. The poem anthologized here is taken from a recently published book edited by Ratti himself.

S. Anand (b. 1972) is the author of a book of poems published by Writers Workshop (Calcutta) which won the Best Prize for Poetry awarded by the Shaeffer Pen Company of the USA through the Workshop. He also authored, at seventeen, a beautiful memory-poem, *Saligrama*, about his grandfather which is still unpublished. Currently a journalist with Hyderabad's *Deccan Chronicle*, he is interested in the Dalit critique of Brahminism.

Sultan Padamsee was a painter and a writer and acted in plays. His poetry is the link between the poetry of Aurobindo and Ezekiel. Aurobindo's mysticism is translated into Padamsee's Christianity (crucified Christ, the javelin-thrusting centurion, Magdalene *et al*). Ezekiel's wry irony is reminiscent of Padamsee.
Sultan died at the age of twenty-three.

Vikram Seth was born in 1952. He trained as an economist and has lived for several years each in England, California, China and India. He is the author of *The Golden Gate: A Novel in Verse, From Heaven Lake: Travels through Sinkiang and Tibet, A Suitable Boy, An Equal Music, Arion and the Dolphin* (a libretto), *Three Chinese Poets* (translations) and four volumes of poetry, including *Beastly Tales from Here and There*.

Vishnu Khandekar (1898-1977), an illustrious writer in Marathi, was awarded the Jnanpith a year before his death for his novel, *Yayati*.

GRATEFUL ACKNOWLEDGEMENT IS MADE TO THE FOLLOWING FOR PERMISSION TO REPRINT COPYRIGHT MATERIAL:

Ashok Row Kavi for 'The Contract of Silence' from *Uncertain Liaisons* edited by Khushwant Singh and Shobha Dé, published by Penguin Books India; Rupa & Co. for 'Shivraj' from *The Street with Fifty-Seven Lanes* by Kamleshwar, translated by Jai Ratan; Katha for *Pages from a Diary* by Bhupen Khakhar, translated by G. N. Devy, from *Katha Prize Stories* vol. 2; Writers Workshop for *O Pomponia Mine, Epithalamium, And So to Bed* from *Poems* by Sultan Padamsee; Madhav G. Gawankar for *The Jungle*; Hoshang Merchant for *The Slaves*; S. Anand for *Poems from a Vacation*; Mahesh Dattani for *Night Queen*; Namdeo Dhasal for *Gandu Bagicha*; R. Raj Rao for *Moonlight Tandoori* from *One Day I Locked My Flat in Soul City*; Parsiana for *A Mermaid called Aida*; Belinder Dhanoa for the extract from *Waiting for Winter* published by Penguin Books India; Bombay Dost for *Underground, Opinions, Bomgay* by R. Raj Rao; Alyson Press, Boston for *Beta* by Rakesh Ratti; Bombay Dost for *Sunshine Trilogy* by Owais Khan; Firdaus Kanga for the extract from *Trying to Grow*; Vikram Seth for the extract from *The Golden Gate,* published by Penguin Books India; R. Raj Rao for *Six Inches*; Adil Jussawala for *Karate, The Raising of Lazarus, Song of a Hired Man*; Gyansingh Shatir for *Never Take Candy from a Stranger!*; Ravi Dayal Publishers for the extract from *Trying to Grow* by Firdaus Kanga; Nusrat Publishers for the extract from *Sheltered Flame* by Iqbal Mateen, translated by Taqi Ali Mirza; .Vishnu Khandekar for the extract from *Yayati,* translated by Nilesh Jahagirdar, published by Popular Prakashan; Gay Men's Press for *Desire brings Sorrow, Under Water, On the Road to Jata Shankar, Apparently* by Dinyar Godrej from *Twenty Something: Poems by Dinyar Godrej, Pat O'Brien and Tim Neave*; Manoj Nair for *Rite of Passage*; Frank Krishner for *The Sweetest of All*; Coach House Press, Canada for *Passage from Africa / A Pass to India* from *The Heat Yesterday* by Ian Iqbal Rashid; Hoshang Merchant for *Autobiography.*